INTERFACE

WHERE O WHERE HAS MY HUGO GONE?
IAN SALES

Each year, the members of the annual World Science Fiction Convention – held this August in Spokane, Washington state, USA – hand out awards in fourteen categories to genre-related works and people, from best novel to best editor to best fan artist. This year "no award" took an unprecedented five categories: novella, short story, related work, editor (short form) and editor (long form). This was a direct consequence of two campaigns by a group of US right-wing writers, Sad Puppies 3 and Rabid Puppies.

Back in 2011, US fantasy writer Larry Correia was shortlisted for the John W Campbell Award for Best New Writer, but failed to win it. The following year, he set up a semi-serious campaign, called Sad Puppies, to get his novel *Monster Hunter Legion* on the Hugo shortlist. He failed. In 2013, he kicked off Sad Puppies 2, but this time the campaign had a more general agenda: the wrong "types" of genre works were winning the Hugo. Finalists were too "literary", they were "message fiction", and they were being nominated solely because of their "political correctness" (a meaningless right-wing smear). Correia's reframing of his campaign as a desire for good old-fashioned adventure of the sort, he claimed, the Hugo used to favour was misguided at best and mendacious at worst. Sad Puppies 2 was much more successful, and managed to place five pieces of fiction on the Hugo ballots, including Correia's most recent novel.

In 2014, Correia handed over the reins to Brad Torgersen, who had been shortlisted twice for the Hugo, thanks to SP2. The narrative changed once again. Now, the Hugos were allegedly controlled by a small clique of "Social Justice Warriors" grouped around either Tor, tor.com, or Tor editors Teresa Nielsen Hayden and Patrick Nielsen Hayden. SP3 was fighting the US culture war.

SP2 had allied itself with Theodore Beale, a toxic trust-fund toy fascist who believes women should be disenfranchised, there's no such thing as marital rape, and Africans are "half-savages", among other equally offensive views. Beale had made the novelette shortlist in 2014, but finished behind "no award". For SP3, Beale created his own version of the campaign, Rabid Puppies. Both sides created slates, ie actual ballots their followers should use to nominate works. These were not lists of suggested works, nor recommendations, they were works and people selected solely by Torgersen and Beale.

SP3/RP was wildly successful, dominating most of the categories on its slates. Beale crony, ultra-Catholic writer John C. Wright, who is prone to homophobic rants, appeared five times. Even Beale appeared twice. In order to defeat a mythical clique which controlled the Hugos, SP3/RP created a clique which…controlled this year's Hugos.

The Worldcon membership – genre fandom itself – was less pleased, however. Thousands of new members join the convention in order to vote. And vote they did. An overwhelming majority rejected the SP3/RP works, in the process demolishing the lie that the SP3/RP campaigns represented the majority of genre fandom.

Finally, a double irony. The winner of the 2015 Hugo for Best Novel, *The Three-Body Problem* by Liu Cixin, only appeared on the shortlist because an author on the SP3 slate withdrew his nomination (he did not want to be associated with SP3/RP). Cixin is a citizen of China. Thanks to a pair of campaigns by right-wing genre fans, the Hugo went for the first time to a translated work by a writer from a communist nation.

They must be really proud of what they've achieved.

interzone

ISSN 0264-3596

Publisher
**TTA Press, 5 Martins Lane,
Witcham, Ely, Cambs CB6 2LB, UK**
w: ttapress.com
e: interzone@ttapress.com
f: facebook.com/TTAPress
t: @TTApress

Editor
Andy Cox
e: andy@ttapress.com

Book Reviews Editor
Jim Steel
e: jim@ttapress.com

Assistant Fiction Editor
Andy Hedgecock

Story Proofreader
Peter Tennant
e: whitenoise@ttapress.com

Events
Roy Gray
e: roy@ttapress.com

Worldwide Distribution
**Pineapple: pineapple-media.com
Central: centralbooks.com
WWMD: specialistmags.co.uk**

Subscriptions & Renewals
The number next to your name
on the address sheet refers to the
final issue of your subscription.
If it's due for renewal you'll see a
mark in the box, and again on an
inserted subscription reminder,
next to the corresponding issue
number. Please renew promptly,
and please do so direct with us
rather than through a third party.

Submissions
Unsolicited submissions of short
stories are always welcome via
our online system, but please be
sure to follow the contributors'
guidelines.

ALL CHANGE by MARTIN HANFORD (2015 COVER ARTIST)
martinhanford1974.deviantart.com

BECKY CHAMBERS: THE LONG WAY TO THE FUTURE
interview by Shaun Green

JONATHAN McCALMONT'S FUTURE INTERRUPTED

HOW TO LOSE FRIENDS AND OBJECTIFY PEOPLE

I recently found myself rewatching 'The Measure of a Man' from the second season of *Star Trek: The Next Generation*. It's the one where the ship's android second-officer Data is ordered to submit to a battery of dangerous tests designed to replicate his neural functions. This process is deemed necessary because reproducing Data's consciousness would allow Starfleet to create hundreds of androids who could be sent into situations deemed too dangerous for mere organics. Data understandably refuses to comply and resigns from Starfleet, at which point Starfleet argues that Data is their property and so can neither resign his commission nor refuse an order. The bulk of the episode is then given over to a court case in which Captain Picard and his first-officer Will Riker argue about whether or not Data should be afforded the same basic rights as any other member of the Federation.

The legal proceedings do eventually (and begrudgingly) conclude that Data is not property but the episode suggests that 24th Century liberals will have grown so morally complacent that they will treat the enslavement of a friend and colleague as a subject worthy of consideration. To make matters worse, the episode also takes place against a backdrop of presenting Data as sympathetic only in so far as he maintains a Pinocchio-like desire to "become human". Whenever the *Enterprise* encounters an artificial lifeform (including Data's identical twin Lore) that does not share this desire, said lifeform is invariably depicted as cold and calculating while non-human individuals who refuse to acknowledge the primacy of human values are treated as moral simpletons and subjected to a torrent of racial abuse that ranges from patronising eye-rolls to overtly racist diatribes about the perils of miscegenation and the horrors of spending too much time surrounded by people from other species.

While science fiction has long enjoyed playing with the question of what it means to be human, the answers it generates always tend to err on the side of inclusion. Even Mary Shelley's *Frankenstein* – thought by some to be the first work of science fiction – features an artificial lifeform asserting his right to a happy life as part of a character arc transporting him from horrible thing to person worthy of understanding and sympathy. This story plays itself out so frequently in the history of science fiction that one could almost argue that aliens, mutants and prehistoric lifeforms were invented to be the kinds of things that turned out to be people after all. Science fiction errs on the side of inclusion because the human capacity for empathy will always expand when left to its own devices. Documentaries like Nicolas Philibert's *Nenette* and James Marsh's *Project Nim* show how natural it is for us to treat apes like people and anyone who has ever owned a cat will know just how easy it can be to fill little fluffy heads with wildly complex psychological states.

'The Measure of a Man' is a fascinating piece of TV as while it too errs on the side of inclusion, it does take seriously the idea that Data might be a thing and so explores the beliefs and thought processes required to look at a friend and colleague and decide that they are not a real person. Academics have a name for the process of reducing people to the state of things; they call it social death.

One of the leading theorists of social death is a sociologist by the name of Zygmunt Bauman. Driven from his native Poland during a wave of anti-Semitic purges in the 1960s, Bauman has written a number of books about the connections between modernity, rationality and social exclusion. Following Freud and Hobbes, Bauman argues that modern societies depend upon people being willing to trade their personal liberties for a sense of collective security. Rationality and modernity are expressions of this trade-off in so far as they are concerned with eliminating uncertainties and creating a world that is understood, regulated and controllable. Society's drive to regulate uncertainty also extends to people and so modern societies go out of their way not only to categorise people according to gender, sexuality and race but also to decide which of these categories contain normal hard-working people and which contain inhuman scum. According to Bauman, the Holocaust was not a return to pre-modern barbarism but a predictable expression of society's existing need to categorise, control and – when appropriate – violently exclude its own constituent parts.

While science fiction has long enjoyed playing with the question of what it means to be human, the answers it generates always tend to err on the side of inclusion

Many of humanity's greatest atrocities have rested upon the assumption that it is possible to provide a definitive answer to the question of what it means to be human. "The Measure of a Man' may end with the vindication of Data's rights but in recognising the court's authority to rule on the question of Data's personhood, the episode unwittingly explores the idea that courts could legitimately wield the power to impose social death and reduce people to the status of objects. By suggesting that lawyers and jurists have a role to play in fixing the boundaries of personhood, 'The Measure of a Man' has tacitly accepted the same assumptions that once underpinned not only America's Jim Crows laws and South Africa's system of Apartheid, but also the anti-Semitic Nuremberg laws that provided the Nazis with a legal framework for determining who did and did not get shipped off to the camps.

Another work that flirts with this type of idea is Alex Garland's recent science fiction film *Ex Machina*. The film opens with fluffy, liberal Caleb flying off to Scandinavia to spend a few days with his boss Nathan; a brilliantly zeitgeisty villain who somehow manages to embody all of the viciousness and fake bonhomie that you'd expect from your average multinational tech company: *Dude...we're like totally best buds and stuff but you really need to sign this form giving me unrestricted access to everything you say, do or write from now until the day you die.*

The film revolves around Nathan's decision to recruit Caleb as the human component in a Turing test. However, as in the case of Data's trial, the test is complete nonsense as the audience recognises the AI's personhood the second she steps on screen. Rather than presenting the audience with anything resembling a valid reason for thinking that 'Eva' might not be worthy of the same rights and freedoms as your average human, the film concerns itself primarily with the relationship between Caleb and Nathan resulting in a wonderfully demented psychological thriller in which Nathan messes so thoroughly with Caleb's head that the poor lad winds up slicing open his own arms in order to make sure that he isn't secretly a robot.

Ostensibly concerned with the same philosophical issues as 'The Measure of a Man', *Ex Machina* echoes and amplifies the problematic elements of that episode in two quite fascinating ways:

Firstly, by presenting the robots as women and having two men compete to determine their fate, the film is inviting us to realise the links between real-world inequalities and the assumption that some people are less than human. Secondly, while Caleb does eventually come to recognise Eva's personhood, he only does so because Eva manages to convince him that she is an appropriate recipient for Caleb's feelings of love. In other words, *Ex Machina* is a film in which women are only recognised as people once they become potential girlfriends. Needless to say, this is not the type of test that anyone would think to apply to Caleb, Nathan or Captain Picard as the white man's humanity is never called into question.

Garland's film is a wonderfully ambiguous and unsettling creation that is best read as stripping works like 'The Measure of a Man' back to their core philosophical components in a way that highlights the ugly racial and gender politics inherent in any attempt to fix the boundaries of personhood. Take out the self-congratulatory tone, the eloquence of Patrick Stewart's oratory and the sense of legitimacy provided by a courtroom setting and what you are left with is the true face of these types of discussion: powerful white men sitting in mansions debating whether or not the women they want to have sex with are actually people. I don't know whether Alex Garland intended *Ex Machina* to be uncomfortable viewing but there is something both intensely familiar and positively inhuman about discussing whether or not someone is actually human.

NINA ALLAN'S TIME PIECES

THE SF OF U AND ME

Last month I wrote a blog post about the recently announced longlist for the Man Booker Prize. Among other things, I grumbled at the paucity of speculative novels from this year's selection. The day after posting the article, I received an email expressing surprise that I hadn't considered Tom McCarthy's *Satin Island* – one of the lucky thirteen – as being of interest to science fiction, and pointing me in the direction of a review by Paul Di Filippo in February's *Locus*.

It wasn't that I'd forgotten McCarthy so much as the fact that I already knew in my bones that *Satin Island* – a single, staunch bastion of modernism in a sea of mostly realist narrative – wouldn't be allowed to get within sniffing distance of the eventual shortlist, let alone the prize itself. (Perhaps McCarthy will win the Goldsmiths, who knows?) Of course I should have talked about McCarthy whatever, and Di Filippo does an excellent and thorough job of explaining why. "A compelling, fascinating monologue," he says of *Satin Island*. "Probably the best J.G. Ballard book not written by JGB himself."

And whilst it is true that *Satin Island*, with its denatured landscapes, its stylised visions of apocalypse, its obsessed, monotonous protagonist, does indeed have a Ballardian vibe about it, it seems to me that this novel and McCarthy's oeuvre in general, which thus far has been discussed mainly in the context of the modernist canon and the ongoing modernism-fail of the British literary establishment, is long overdue for a reappraisal in the light of its science

fictionality. The more I think about this, the more it seems clear that *Satin Island* belongs to an under-discussed category of British science fiction that might accurately be termed post-Ballardian. That the works making up this canon also share an allegiance to modernism and to new ways of formulating fiction should come as no surprise. Ballard's enthusiasm for conceptual art and for the breaking down of conventionally 'literary' modes of expression is well known. That writers with an intellectual or aesthetic kinship to Ballard might choose a similarly skewed approach to questions of realism should be taken almost for granted.

The narrator of *Satin Island* is a Present-Tense Anthropologist named U. Briefly famous for assembling a landmark treatise on club culture, U is currently employed by a company known as the Company and tasked with putting together a Great Report. What this report is to comprise is never made clear. We know only that it is "finding its form", that it is an analysis of Life, the Universe and Everything as required for universally feasible business models. The Great Report will enable U's paymaster, Peyman, to Sell More Stuff. More crucially, the Great Report will so accurately predict what we're minded – genetically, habitually, notionally – to purchase that it will enable the Company to bypass the selling stage and move straight along to unquantifiables, which is almost certainly where the biggest profits are to be made.

U compiles a number of mini-reports – on oil slicks, on the

seemingly-random-but-perhaps-not deaths of parachutists – in an attempt to discern an overall pattern in the nature of being. There is a hilarious description – and one that will be immediately familiar to all writers – of U decluttering his desk in preparation for the Real Work that is about to take place there. There is a disturbing and completely unexplained account by U's girlfriend Madison of an incident in her past when she was subjected to police brutality and sublimated rape following a G8 protest. If you're thinking that this all sounds like Ballard to a T, and that U could quite easily be one of Ballard's mad doctors, then you'd be thinking in the right direction. For me though, there's something in McCarthy's vision that moves beyond Ballard, through anarchy and into entropy. If Ballard's landscapes are blasted by the light of a sun gone rogue, then McCarthy's interior voids – you'd be surprised how infrequently U ever seems to go outside – are bathed in the dead-eyed fluorescence of halogen bulbs.

McCarthy's reviewers are at pains to point out his "anti-humanism", his apparent un-interest in anything resembling a social narrative. McCarthy's dialogue, they insist, is with the impossibility of self-expression in a universe where the self as such does not exist and where human beings, at least in the literary sense, represent not so much souls made flesh as "nodes of behaviour". None of this should detract from the fact that whether he meant to or not, McCarthy has constructed a novel of intense

human interest. *Satin Island* presents a vision of the future we are walking towards that is far more chilling than anything you'll find in any common-or-garden dystopia or post-apocalypse. The world of Peyman's Koob Sassen Project is already functioning all around us, mimicking, *replacing* reality as the oil slicks U studies so obsessively mimic and replace the substance and action of the actual ocean.

If the content of *Satin Island* could be distilled down to one broadly comprehensible science fictional message, it would be that we missed our boss battle with the Borg because we've already been assimilated *without even noticing*.

No one is ever going to love *Satin Island* – it's hard to love something as cold and remorseless as titanium steel – but as a Great Report on what the novel can be in the twenty-first century it is effortlessly persuasive and – if McCarthy doesn't mind me using such a dirty word – impassioned.

And there are others who share McCarthy's vision. If we consider Tobias Hill's 2003 novel *The Cryptographer*, for example, we find a similar preoccupation with corporate assimilation of private spaces. The protagonist of this novel, Anna, works for the Inland Revenue and even likes

If the content of *Satin Island* could be distilled down to one broadly comprehensible science fictional message, it would be that we missed our boss battle with the Borg because we've already been assimilated *without even noticing*

it. She enjoys the process of her work, its inherent logic. But her values and loyalties are thrown into question when she is tasked with investigating the eponymous cryptographer, a mega-rich code-writer named John Law whose wealth and international business credentials conveniently serve to place him above suspicion. Anna is faced with the choice of not exploring a numerical anomaly, or risking the collapse of the entire greater-capitalist world economy.

Similarly, the protagonist of Will Wiles's 2014 novel *The Way Inn* starts off as a happy cog in a smoothly functioning machine. Neil Double *likes* the machine, the machine keeps him comfortable and moderately stimulated. His job as a conference surrogate makes him a more or less permanent denizen of the curious between-world composed of business centres, airport concourses and corporate hotels. When the gears of the machine slip and Neil finds himself caught between them, he quickly discovers far more than he ever wanted to about what ultimately lies behind the Way Inn's bland facade.

To his credit and to our satisfaction, Neil decides to resist. Anyone who has ever done fruitless battle with the recorded drones servic-

ing a call centre will be high-fiving this protagonist all the way. Even if the monsters ultimately win, Neil Double is not going down without a fight. And it is here that McCarthy's vision diverges most distressingly from that of his antecedents. Ballard's fiction, which even more than an analogue of the future was a rationalisation of its author's past trauma, wears its violence brashly, sometimes intoxicatingly on its sleeve: shots are fired, cities are drowned, obsessions, unlike U's Great Report, really do find their form. There is a dramatic tension in Ballard – a lack of closure – that is a challenge to the future, rather than a capitulation.

The conclusion of *The Cryptographer* hints at a new, post-capitalist world order. In *The Way Inn*, Neil Double is on the run but he has friends and more even than that he has plans. He is *alive*. Even Kafka's hapless heroes – Gregor Samsa, K – railed against the fundamental inequalities in the systems that crushed them. U cannot see the point of overthrowing the system because he is already so fully acclimatised to the consensus reality that he cannot imagine anything better or more meaningful. His fantasies of violence – of headbutting the minister who spouts inaccurate nonsense at a colleague's funeral, of bringing down the Company – remain just that: fantasies.

> To go to Staten Island – actually go there – would have been profoundly meaningless. What would it, in reality, have solved, or resolved? Nothing. (p 170)

Forget *The Walking Dead*. The bleeding edge of science fiction is *Satin Island*.

DAVID LANGFORD'S ANSIBLE LINK

Worldcon. At Sasquan, the 2015 World SF Convention in Spokane, there was a pervading smoky reek from Washington State's wildfires (Kevin J. Anderson: 'Sigh. Some fan group must be doing human sacrifices again'). Site selection voters gave the 2017 Worldcon to Helsinki with 1363 votes; Washington DC received 878, Montréal 228 and Japan 120. Amid quips from co-MC David Gerrold (who said George R.R. Martin was in the audience but no longer on Twitter because he killed all 140 characters), the Campbell award for best new writer went to Wesley Chu and the Hugos to... Fan Artist: Elizabeth Leggett. Fan Writer: Laura J. Mixon. Fancast: *Galactic Suburbia Podcast*. Fanzine: *Journey Planet*. Semiprozine: *Lightspeed*. Professional Artist: Julie Dillon. Professional Editor, Short Form: No Award. Professional Editor, Long Form: No Award. Graphic Story: *Ms. Marvel, Volume 1*. Related Work: No Award. Dramatic, Short (presented by a Dalek): *Orphan Black*, 'By Means Which Have Never Yet Been Tried'. Dramatic, Long: *Guardians of the Galaxy*. Short Story: No Award. Novelette: Thomas Olde Heuvelt, 'The Day the World Turned Upside Down' (*Lightspeed*). Novella: No Award. Novel (presented via video from the International Space Station): Cixin Liu, *The Three Body Problem*. A record turnout of 5950 ballots rejected the controversial 'Puppies' slates which had exploited a nominating loophole to sweep many categories: No Award took the five all-slate categories and no slate nominee won elsewhere, except *Guardians of the Galaxy* with its far broader popularity.

George R.R. Martin, homaging his characters' gory deaths in *Game of Thrones*, makes a cameo appearance in *Sharknado 3: Oh Hell No!* 'as a moviegoer who gets brutally attacked by a shark that somehow jumps out of the movie screen and into his face.' (Cnet. com)

As Others Invoke Us. Comparing one famously clownish figure with another: 'In a rough year for polling analysis, the Trump surge stands out. The first-time candidate whom so many people wrote off has done for 2016 what Isaac Asimov's Mule did for the psycho-historians of Foundation – a conquest from out of nowhere, unpredicted by any of the calculations, turning his enemies' blasted palaces into new (and classy) throne rooms.' (*Washington Post*)

Amy Schumer, US comedian, annoyed the galactic overlords of *Star Wars* by appearing dressed as Princess Leia in a naughty *GQ* magazine photo feature: in bed with ardent C-3PO and R2-D2, in a high-kicking chorus line with Imperial Stormtroopers, etc. 'Lucasfilm & Disney didn't approve, participate in or condone the inappropriate use of our characters in this manner,' thundered the *Star Wars* Twitter feed. (BBC)

More Awards. *Gemmell* (heroic fantasy). Novel: Brandon Sanderson, *Words of Radiance*. Debut: Brian Stavely, *The Emperor's Blades*. Cover: Sam Green for *Words of Radiance*. • *Locus Awards* for novels. SF: Ann Leckie, *Ancillary Sword*. Fantasy: Katherine Addison, *The Goblin Emperor*. Debut: Mary Rickert, *The Memory Garden*. • *Munsey* (pulp-related): Steve Miller. • *Mythopoeic* (fantasy). Adult: Sarah Avery, *Tales from Rugosa Coven*. Children: Natalie Lloyd, *A Snicker of Magic*. Scholarship, Inklings: Robert Boenig, *C.S. Lewis and the Middle Ages*. Scholarship, Other: Brian Attebery, *Stories About Stories: Fantasy and the Remaking of Myth*. • *Prometheus* (libertarian): Daniel Suarez, *Influx*. • *SF Poetry Association Grand Master*: Marge Simon, Steve Sneyd. • *Sidewise* (alternate history). Long: Kristine Kathryn Rusch, *The Enemy Within*. Short: Ken Liu, 'The Long Haul: From the Annals of Transportation, The Pacific Monthly, May 2009' (*Clarkesworld*). • *World Fantasy Life Achievement*: Ramsey Campbell, Sheri S. Tepper.

Career Advice to fugitives from US justice: don't star in even a low-budget horror film under your own name, as did bank robber Jason Stange in *Marla Mae* (forthcoming 2016). Police relentlessly noticed him in advance-publicity photos, and pounced. (BBC)

As Others Criticise. '…*Jurassic World* epitomises four-quadrant-striving boardroom-delegated moviemaking and the quagmire resulting from fan-expectation-driven supersizing that's endemic to sequel-making and "rebooting."' (*Sight & Sound*)

Michael Moorcock's July *New Statesman* profile/interview had a subhead saying he 'revolutionised

science fiction with symbolism, sex and psychoactive drugs.' Also included was the mandatory quotation 'I think Tolkien was a crypto-fascist'. Later MM issued a disclaimer about having not been entirely accurately quoted … 'Oh, and I absolutely LOVE hobbits. I'm just looking for the best recipe.'

J.R.R. Tolkien is now commemorated on maps of Saturn's moon Titan, where by IAU convention the mountains are named for Middle-earth's and the hills for its characters: hence Mountains of Moria (Moria Montes) and Gandalf Hills (Gandalf Colles). Freta, straits or channels, get the

names of characters in Asimov's *Foundation* series.

I Say It's Spinach. 'Popeye is very, very similar to these medieval sculptures. You have a sense of transcendence taking place here. Here with Popeye it's transcendence of male energy. He eats that spinach and he transcends into the strength. And I think, you know, that's the art; the spinach is art.' (Jeff Koons in *Imagine … Jeff Koons: Diary of a Seducer*, BBC1)

The Weakest (Topical) Link. 'What is the title of the third book in the *Hunger Games* trilogy?' Contestant: '*To Kill a Mockingbird*.' (BBC2, *Two Tribes*)

 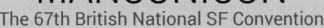

F.W. Murnau, director of the classic vampire film *Nosferatu* (1922), was news again in July with reports that his skull was stolen from his grave in Stahnsdorf cemetery near Berlin. (BBC) In a Tim Powers novel there'd be excellent magical reasons for this theft, and others too would lose random body parts.

As Others Invoke Us. Charles Bukowski on Henry Miller: '*Star Trek* contemplation sperm-jizz babble'. (C. Bukowski, *On Writing* [posthumous], 2015)

Court Circular. The iron jack-boot of Disney descended on the British 'Joker's Masquerade' fancy-dress retailer, which has long used starwars.co.uk and related domains for (licensed) themed costumes. Disney complained to Nominet, which ruled in its favour and called the registration 'abusive'. An appeal will follow. (BBC)

George Lucas is among those receiving 2015 lifetime honours from the John F. Kennedy Center for Performing Arts. The ceremony, hosted by some chap called Obama, will be in December. (BBC)

Thog's Masterclass. *Pluto Revealed!* 'Originally it revolved around another sun, some star which was light-years away. How it tore loose from that star we'll probably never know – the star might have simply become too dim, their planet might have been on a shaky orbit, an experiment of theirs might have jarred it loose, many things could have happened.' (Donald A. Wollheim, *The Secret of the Ninth Planet*, 1959) • *Conceptual Breakthrough Dept.* 'His brain began to sway on its base, as the landslide of possibilities unreeled before it.' (A.E. van Vogt, 'Juggernaut', August 1944 *Astounding*) • *Mot Juste Dept.* 'Rugolo glanced at the greenness carpeting the plain, which he had taken to be a variety of grass or moss, forms of verbiage common on many worlds…' (Barrington J. Bayley, *Eye of Terror*, 1999) • *Dept of Baleful Dessert.* '…a face pink and stern as frozen strawberry custard.' (Ayn Rand, *Ideal*, written 1934; published 2015)

R.I.P.

Robert Conquest (1917–2015), Anglo-American author and historian best known for documenting Soviet atrocities under Stalin, died on 3 August; he was 98. His sf novel is *A World of Difference* (1955); with long-time friend Kingsley Amis he co-edited the five *Spectrum* sf anthologies (1961–1966), whose verse epigraphs include his famous "'Sf's no good," they bellow till we're deaf. / "But this looks good." – "Well then, it's not sf." His *The Abomination of Moab* (1979) collects these verses and other essays including sf criticism.

E.L. Doctorow (1931–2015), noted US author of historical fiction who used fantastic themes in *Big as Life* (1966) and the steampunkish *The Waterworks* (1994), died on 21 July; he was 84.

Toby English, British book dealer who used to sell sf/fantasy in UK convention dealers' rooms, died from cancer on 25 July. His shop in Wallingford had closed earlier in 2015.

Steve Kennedy (1945–2015), US art dealer who specialised in pulp and represented various artists (or their estates) including Hannes Bok, Rafael DeSoto and J. Allen St. John, died on 4 July aged 70.

Alan Kupperberg (1953–2015), US comics artist who worked on several titles for Marvel (*Defenders, Invaders, Punisher, Spider-Man, Thor, X-Men* etc) and later DC (including *Justice League of America*), died on 17 July aged 62.

Adrienne Martine-Barnes (1942–2015), US author who began publishing fiction in 1982 and produced both solo novels and multiple collaborations with Marion Zimmer Bradley and Diana L. Paxson, died on 23 July.

Jef Murray (1960–2015), US artist who illustrated Tolkien and C.S. Lewis, died unexpectedly on 3 August aged 55.

Jeff Rice (1944–2015), best known as creator of the TV series *Kolchak: The Night Stalker* (1974–1975), died on 1 July aged 71. The series pilot was *The Night Stalker* (1972), adapted by Richard Matheson from Rice's then-unpublished novel of the same title which appeared in 1973.

John A. Williams (1925–2015), US writer and poet whose sf novels – beginning with *The Man Who Cried I Am* (1967) – focused on America's racial conflicts, died on 3 July; he was 89.

Markus Wolfson (pseudonym of Mark McCann, 1945–2015), UK author of *The Magonia Stone* (2015) and a number of short stories, died of cancer on 30 June; he was 69.

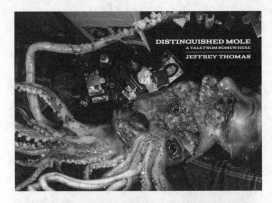

BLACK STATIC #48 OUT NOW

Fiction
JEFFREY THOMAS
CATE GARDNER
STEVEN J. DINES
ANDREW HOOK
STEPHEN BACON

Interviewed
SIMON KURT UNSWORTH

Comment
LYNDA E. RUCKER
STEPHEN VOLK

Book & DVD/BD Reviews
PETER TENNANT
TONY LEE

Art
MARTIN HANFORD
JOACHIM LUETKE
RICHARD WAGNER
TARA BUSH

Coming Soon
RALPH ROBERT MOORE
THANA NIVEAU
STEPHEN HARGADON
TIM LEES
ERINN L. KEMPER
V.H. LESLIE
TYLER KEEVIL

"One of the sharpest looking magazines on the racks" BLACK GATE

"The best international magazine of dark fiction. No other magazine in existence matches it in quality of fiction, columns, and visual appeal" HORROR WORLD

"The most essential publication for fans of literary horror" DREAD CENTRAL

"Continues to be the best horror magazine out there" ELLEN DATLOW

"One of the top magazines in the field of horror and dark fiction" HELLNOTES

ADD BLACK STATIC TO YOUR INTERZONE SUBSCRIPTION:
ttapress.com/shop/

ILLUSTRATED BY RICHARD WAGNER

JOHN SHIRLEY
WEEDKILLER

1. CHARLIE VENTER

The squid balloon was hovering over East L.A., a mile past downtown. The sky was like a gray steel lid, as it usually was. Venter's observer was hovering just under the thickest layer of haze from the sea's gradual evaporation. Venter remembered, in childhood, L.A. had been famed for its clear, sunny days. Now the palm trees were shriveled and brown from lack of sun.

He looked back at his console. Despite the gloom he was getting a crisp, clear camera shot.

There they were, the two possibles marked, red brackets on the screen following them as they ran. *Sheldon Ivy* and *Dino Chou, I.D. confirmed.* One of the possibles had to die, Ivy or Chou; it didn't matter, really, which one.

The wind changed course, making the squid balloon's cab shake and sway. Immediately the vessel's jets countered, and the computer-controlled inflated arms shifted to compensate, each inflated vane angling to shunt wind around it and create a pocket of stability.

The cab stabilized, returned to position, and Venter narrowed from the squidcam to drone cam. He could see the possibles even more clearly now, running across the fallen roof of the collapsed parking structure.

He had the weaponry, of course, to shoot one dead from up here – if he were permitted to. But it was only allowed in specific circumstances. They had to locate actual hardcore criminals. In a case like this he was only certified for weedkilling. Targets had to be given the CMSC – the Crisis Management Social Context statement – and the operative had to read part three of it with them, out loud.

Both this guy Ivy and this Chou would be paralyzed from the neck up, when he set it up with them to read. So they wouldn't have anything else to do but read along with part three, or beg for their lives. And begging was strictly discouraged, since it was futile and time wasting.

The possibles had crossed into the remains of the old shopping mall, most of it flattened in the same tornado that had leveled much of East Los Angeles. He could remember people being amazed at seeing tornados in Southern California. Now they were routine.

The wind was picking up, but his instruments predicted only a low level storm. Still, the squid balloon could only adjust so much. He needed to go down, out of the wind, and settle matters with the possibles.

He started down, got below the fiercest wind, confirmed his LZ – and found he was hesitating about setting the squid balloon down.

Christine. Seeing her on Mei's lap; his half Chinese daughter, his Chinese wife, the toddler sitting on her mom's lap in the Chinese restaurant with Mei's parents, everyone smiling as Mei fed her with chopsticks. A shrine to Buddha on the counter in the background; a white-aproned waiter carrying steaming food to another table.

Lucky people.

"Venter, are you losing focus?"

It was the friendly male voice of Pilot Monitoring. When you had two incidents of failed closing in a year, they put the watch program on you.

"No, I'm not losing focus," he told the monitoring program. He continued his descent, feeling his stomach clench, his heart thump.

"I see that descent is continuing," said the monitor. "Have you located an optimum LZ?"

He glanced at the flight modeler. "Yes, I think so. Yes."

"I don't see any indication you've used the recommended Empadown dosing, Venter."

"How did—" Then he remembered that the medical cabinet in the balloon cab's bathroom dispensed all the requested pills, noted them and sent a report to monitoring. "Oh yeah. Well, they were irritating my stomach."

"Are you feeling nausea? Is vertigo returning?"

"No vertigo."

"We strongly recommend you take your Empadown."

"I'm not actually required to take the pills if I…well…"

Don't argue with it, he told himself. *Mei and Christine are counting on you. Can't lose this job.*

Mei had said it to him, just the other morning. *Millions of people wish they had the kind of pay and security you have, Charlie…*

She was better at partitioning feelings than he was, and it really was a vital job skill.

"Your chance of successfully completing this assignment correctly is significantly increased if you take the Empadown," the monitor said.

Venter exhaled a long, windy breath. "I'll take it, soon as I've set down," he told the monitor.

The anti-empathy pill would give him nausea. Maybe the psyche evaluation had been right. Mei's father had pulled strings to get him this job after his evaluator hadn't recommended him. *He is simply psychologically unsuited*, the report had said.

Venter set the balloon down, checked perimeters for risk factors, secured the anchors, and then went to the medicine cabinet.

Just get this over with and go home. Go home to Christine. And Mei.

2. SHARON DE LOS SANTOS

The sleep mod shut off promptly at 7 a.m. Sharon woke within seconds, got up, hurried through the small, almost unfurnished apartment to the bathroom, urinated, then came back to bed, stretched out, still wearing her yellowing rancid pajamas, and put her face right in the mask first thing. Having slept, she was close enough to rested and her reflexes would be sharp, and she wasn't going to waste a second of it.

The mask had a charged food-and-fluid tube in it. She sucked up the contents of the tube, swallowed, and muttered the intensity settings. The mask was already set to uChan 8785789358937 5893; it would go there instantly once in activation. She felt jets of excitement, anticipation, her pulse already rising. She activated the channel.

She saw the logo, titles, Experiential Production credits, blah blah, so fucking what, get to the uChan. Then 87857893589375893 went off like a shotgun blast from every direction at once, input and prompting, image and cues, icons and symbols, threats and evasions, tactile sensations, noise and music, light and shadow, and smells – the *smells*! Acrid and sweet odors, alternating like discordant notes and harmonious notes in a buzzrock cut; burning tires, sweat, perfume, a cool spring breeze that carried, after a moment, the tang of urine cooking in a doorway catching

the sunlight; the distant rasp of gunpowder from a shotgun shell; a wisp of daffodils from some tiny park. Her head hurt but her mind resolved the image and in an instant she was in a standard Chinatown, feeling the sidewalk under her boots, walking in her skintight jumpsuit under signs both cryptic and familiar; passing a herbal medicine shop; heart pounding as she turned the corner and the big steel grille on the onrushing vehicle bounding right at her as the Hydrogen Caddy jumped the curb, the big slab of car bearing down as she leapt up, her avatar's legs far more agile and strong than her real limbs in the meat world and she was on the hood of the car running over its windshield and roof as it raced over the spot she'd stood in; she jumped off a split second before it collided with the brick wall and someone cursed in Chinese as the car gouged through the corner of the building and crushed a bent elderly Chinese lady, the wet, messy accident visible though it was behind because Sharon had 360. She saw pigeons flying up in a spray of flapping dirty gray anxiety over the dying woman – but already she was leaving the accident behind, dodging across the street to the slightly open door as a helicopter flew by overhead and crosshairs tracked her back.

She was through the door and dodging through the passages, then up a stairway, to the roof. And here the *exphase* cut in, and she was seeing herself from the helicopter that was monitoring her, seeing herself through the scope of a sniper rifle aimed through the open door, trying to get a bead on herself – she shifted, wrenching into another point of view, and suddenly she was the pilot of the helicopter, seeing the city whirl panoramically below as she circled back to the rooftop where the target was rolling to avoid a shot that just grazed her; she felt herself rolling and glimpsed herself from the helicopter, both at once, saw and felt herself cannon-balling through a skylight. And as she smashed down through the glass the fall went all slow motion as jagged shards spun around her, glinting, reflecting her image over and over, and then she struck the gunman who was waiting below, knocked him flat with the heels of her boots...as she flew the helicopter over the city and glanced up at the police skimmer, the flying motorcycle operated by a woman cop who was tracking her.

Sharon gunned the copter and the skimmer gave chase as she saw an elevated train flashing by below…which she was driving at exactly the proper speed; she was braking the train, but not fast enough because up ahead someone was on the track, it was her, Sharon's avatar: she'd run from the building where she'd crashed through the skylight, was struggling with a masked man on the tracks, feeling his powerful arms pressing her down, the man shouting *We'll both die here and I'm glad, I want out of this channel* and she yelled *I want to stay here forever* and she kicked him off into the path of the train which one of her avatars was driving, looking away as the train crushed the man but out of the corner of her eye seeing herself vaulting up onto the platform, just ahead of the train…

Sharon was distantly aware that the VR mask was running coolant, was swabbing her sweat away, as she lay, in the real world, on the mattress. She felt a headache rising, pounding like drum percussion increasing its tempo. She ignored it.

Sharon, in uChan 87857893589375893, dodged between people crowding onto the train platform, looking for an egress, an exit, a way out…a way out…

3. CHARLIE VENTER

The Empadown had kicked in. Loping through the culvert, Venter was starting to feel the thrill of the chase. He had been trained to encourage that feeling in himself, and the frisson was like chilled metal along his spine as he glanced down at the tracer screen. It was dark in here; he'd put on his light harvest goggles, and still it was dim, but he could see their silhouettes now, jogging ahead of him.

Did they know he was here? They knew he was after them. They'd seen the balloon. They hadn't taken a shot at it, but there was no breaking its high-flex materials with bullets, and they probably knew that. They'd been hiding from weedkillers for a year now.

His boots splashed in murky water; he could smell its rankness. Water seeped between seams in the culvert. And then a glow pushed at his eyes, blotting everything for a moment, and he tugged the goggles down so they hung around his neck. Up ahead the culvert ended in a tumble of stone. He could see the tops of the apartment complex beyond it – Ivy and Chou were heading back into the occupied part of the city, maybe hoping to lose themselves in a crowd somewhere. If they saw how close he was they might try to turn on him, lay in wait somewhere…

Venter emerged from the culvert into the muggy dull-gray outer world, and saw that he'd lost sight of them. But there was still dust rising from the mound of rubble, where they'd clambered over.

Ten minutes more, with his own fast breathing in his ears, his backpack feeling like it was getting heavier as he climbed over broken concrete and strode quickly down a row of mostly collapsed single family homes, not seeing his possibles. Campfire smoke rose from a house missing its roof, but that wouldn't be them.

He was vulnerable here, trotting along in the open on this cracked, slime coated sidewalk. He considered calling in a back up team, but he lost pay points if he did that, and he was already flagged in HR as a potential problem. The squid balloons were expensive, were supposed to be reserved for the highly rated weedkillers. He could end up back on a three-wheeler driving through the streets all day looking for the homeless, for drug addicts and schizophrenics to weed out.

He felt his stomach do a flip-flop – the Empadowns. He ducked between two deserted houses, took his tracer screen from his pack, and called up to the squid balloon's drone for a target location.

The scanner in the balloon cab had kept track of them; they were about five blocks ahead and one to the left. They were climbing over a fence into the occupied area. As he watched from the drone above them they ducked behind a car, flattened as housing security drove by. The instant the car turned a corner they got up and ran full out toward a high rise. Right up to the front door.

Venter was pretty sure they didn't live there – but someone let them in, at the front door.

Good. They had gone to ground – and now he knew where to find them.

4. SHARON DE LOS SANTOS

She could feel the wind whipping her hair as she accelerated the streakbike, roaring through a tunnel helmetless, racing a grinning young man in blue leather on a blue streakbike. Their bikes weaved between the cars and out of the tunnel and she looked back to see the blue rider, thinking maybe a hookup but then he pointed to warn her and she turned to see she'd wandered from her lane and was going to hit the back of an electric SUV; she screamed as she struck it, wrenched herself into an avatar running breathlessly through the back door of the hotel, and up two flights to the safe room…where the door responded to her thumbprint.

She saw he was waiting there, coming out of the bathroom, wet from a shower; his blue leather riding togs were flung on the floor. Still panting from her run she ran into his arms and his embrace. She stripped off her clothes and within seconds they were coupling and she was barely aware of the sound of the chopper flying by the window – the helicopter she was piloting, feeling the lovemaking experienced by the avatar in the hotel room. The sensation made it tough to pilot the aircraft and she almost crashed on the hotel roof so she shifted that point of view to a dancer spinning through a club as she danced with another woman, around and around, but feeling the man's hands gentle and firm on her body, in the hotel room, and then someone was coming out of the dance room crowd, stalking toward her with a gun, and—

The mask, scanning her physical functions, knew Sharon had taken on too much and was about to vomit; it lifted gently out of the way, on its frame struts, and she turned over and threw up, only then realizing that she'd writhed from the bed onto the floor. She heaved again and again, sobbing, then, panting, she got up, went to the bathroom to wash out her mouth. She was careful not to look in the mirror while she was at the sink, as she very much did not want to see the woman whose hair was falling out, the woman who looked to be in her late eighties whereas, in fact, she was only forty-three.

She cleaned up, drank a little water, took a trank-and-stim and then went back to the mask lying beside the bed. She made some adjustments to the mask, put it on, lay back on the mattress, and activated uChan 87857893589375893-B.

But then the mask shut off. Sharon was staring into fizzing pixels.

"*Security override. Someone is attempting to break into your apartment,*" said her own voice on her headset.

She gave out a wordless yell of frustration and sat up, tore the mask off, panting, hands shaking.

"That's bullshit," she said. She'd forgotten she had put the security override on the mask. She'd done it so long ago. Years. "It's bullshit!" she hissed, throwing the mask down.

But she heard a grating sound, then, from the front door of her high rise apartment, and it was like the key was turning right between her eyes, grinding through her skull.

Get a grip, Sharon. Someone's trying to use an actual key. She'd set up a wipe-card lock, two years ago. Or was it five years?

Mouth dry, hands shaking, Sharon went to the door, and listened. She heard a voice she recognized. "I don't know, key turns, but nothing, it doesn't unlock." Cabello, that short fat maintenance guy who wouldn't climb two flights of stairs when the elevator was broken. She'd seen him once this year and he'd said she looked sick, said maybe she should go to the clinic and she told him to kiss her ass and ducked into the elevator.

"She's got a wipe lock now, man." An unfamiliar voice. Sounded like a young man. "You sure she's not there?"

"No she gotta be either dead or—"

A wave of fury rose up in her and she snarled "Open!" at the lock. The door popped inward and three men stepped back, startled.

I shouldn't have done that. They could be murderers, rapists.

But she was raw and adrenalized and angry. They'd yanked her out of the mask; torn her from the uChan.

Then she saw the looks on their faces. Three of them, only one she knew: stubby roundfaced Cabello, the maintenance man. With him, looking taut, hands clenched, was a sandy-haired young guy, maybe twenty, spiky beard, and an Asian-Hispanic mix with glossy waist-length black hair and an animated tattoo on his forearm: a train endlessly crashing into a wall.

Their faces were pinched – Cabello had a hand over his mouth. They were reacting to *the smell*.

"Jeez, lady!" Cabello said.

"Don't start!" she barked at him. "It's my place, I'll keep it how I want. Now…" She closed her eyes and the words kind of squirted out of her mouth. "Why are you here?"

She opened her eyes and glared. *Just get rid of them.*

Cabello raised a chubby short-fingered hand. "Hey, we made a mistake. I didn't see any life signs. The indicator – nothing."

She remembered. She'd had one of her fits of paranoia, after a long jag under the mask, and she'd turned off the life signs indicator. She'd cut the wire, really, though that was illegal.

"I didn't think you were around no more," Cabello said. "I saw you, what, six months ago. You don't go shopping or nothing so—"

"I have food delivered!" Sharon said.

"But no soap," the sandy haired guy muttered, looking worriedly down the hall to Sharon's right.

He had the look of someone on the run, she decided. He was more in danger than dangerous.

Wait – Cabello said six months? Was it that long?

She felt dizzy now, weak, as the trank-and-stim wore off. And the old familiar feeling of self-disgust was welling up in her, like a toilet overflowing.

"Lady," the Asian kid said. "The weedkiller's looking for us. Can we come in for a few hours? He can't go into every room. Cabello'll tell him a story. He'll move on."

She leaned on the door frame, arms crossed over her chest, and looked at Cabello. He seemed unreal. Less real than something on uChan.

He took her expression as accusation. "Weedkiller got one of my girls." Cabello shrugged apologetically. "I don't like those balloon *cabrones*. I know Dino here, since he was a kid. He grew up in the building right across the—"

"I don't *care*, Cabello! I can't have anyone in here."

"She's right," said the weedkiller, coming down the hall from her left – padding rapidly along, his paralyzer in his left hand, his right on a holstered pistol. The paralyzer was just a tube ending in a prong; they turned up in uChan stories sometimes. He had a crisp blue and gray uniform, pant legs tucked into his boots; neat government issue utility pack on his back. He was a stocky, wide-faced man with flat, expressionless eyes; his pocked cheeks were reddened and he was breathing hard. He'd come up the stairs instead of the elevator. "Everyone do *not* move. I am Agent Charles Venter, Crisis Management, Winnowing. Sheldon Ivy and Dino Chou, you are both under consideration for possible—"

All at once, the young guy who was probably Sheldon turned to sprint down the hall, Dino started to push past Sharon into the apartment, and Cabello threw himself flat on the carpeted hall floor and covered his head.

Sharon instinctively blocked Dino, who didn't try to force her out of the way – and then the paralyzer made the air glitter for one nearly imperceptible moment, and Dino's back arched; he fell back, twisting, onto Sheldon. Together they hit the floor hard enough to make it shake.

Then they lay there in the hall, stretched out, a stiff tangle of limbs, paralyzed. How long would the paralysis last? Five minutes or a little more? That's what she'd heard.

Cabello was looking up at the glowering weedkiller. "They said they knew her! This lady here! They were… She was…"

Venter shook his head. "You're lying, Mr Cabello. You lost a daughter, so you helped these two. Get out of here, and maybe I won't report it. Just be ready to take out the body bag. That's on you. I'll send it down on the elevator." He pointed down the hall toward the elevators.

Cabello was up with uncharacteristic speed, stepping over the quivering fallen men, hurrying away. Sharon thought she heard him sob but she wasn't sure.

She thought, *I should close the door now. Go in and lay down…*

But she could smell her own apartment now; she could smell her own body. She had lost any awareness of the funk of her rooms herself, till this moment. And she could see her withered hands on the door frame. She wanted to run, to follow Cabello. But she felt paralyzed, too. She straightened up a little, to make sure the device hadn't affected her somehow. She wasn't paralyzed like that. She was just kind of locked up inside.

It's all in my mind, she thought.

It was. But – it didn't matter. She had come to some kind of wall in herself. It was like the time she'd been riding in a self-driving car and its guidance system had outdated information, it took a turn onto a road that had been washed away, the farther end cut off by a flood, because of the climate extremes, and the car kept driving and driving to the end of the road. She had been afraid it wouldn't stop. The self-drive sedan seemed to be rushing at that big shining Road Ends sign…

"Crisis management," Dino said, his voice hoarse. "Perpetual crisis. Forever crisis. A crisis – it's not supposed to last forever."

Venter was down on one knee now, his backpack leaning against the wall. He was putting the paralyzer into the pack, slipping the tube neatly into a nylon sling, and taking out a screen pad.

"You've been sent the notices, as per the Crisis Management Act," Venter said, in a calm, businesslike voice, "but I am required to read part three with you, as per concern for human dignity."

"That's funny, right there," Sheldon rasped. "Human dignity!"

Venter started toward them – then he sniffed, and stopped, eyebrows arched; turned toward Sharon. She could tell he was taking in her matted hair, her premature aging, her stained pajamas. And the smell.

"Ma'am, you need to go in and close the door."

She still couldn't get herself to move. The end of the side road was close. "He's right," she said. "You – your function…it's absurd. Weeding out a few people here and there isn't going to…" She shook her head.

Venter didn't look offended or surprised. He'd heard it all before. Probably he'd thought it all before, too. "Nine billion plus people, ma'am. Climate change. Loss of arable land, billions of people displaced – endless food and housing emergencies. Constant crisis – not of my making, okay? Would you go in, please?"

"But you can't make a dent in nine billion by picking out people who aren't productive and… there would have to be a billion agents and there aren't." She badly wanted some water. Her throat felt burnt, her tongue thick. She needed water and tranquilizers and sleep. But she felt pinned in the doorway.

He stared at her. "Did you catch some paralyzer current?"

"No." She moved her body around, waved her arms over her head, aware that it was comic. She was absurd, too. "See?"

"Then go inside and close the door. I have the authority to paralyze you, and fine you."

"Answer my question – how can you make a dent in that much populace? Tell me that and maybe I'll go in."

He glanced at his watch. "I gave them seven minutes but we're going to run out of my allotted time. Then I may have to shoot one of them with a gun and that'll hurt them. You don't want that, do you? It'll be painless otherwise."

"Just answer me!" She was surprised at her own stridency. "I met these boys, just now. I…" It was hard to explain – how she'd come out of the mask, raging inside, and then she found all this on her doorstep and it felt like it wasn't an accident; it felt like it was here for her to find. "I need to know this."

"There's an algorithm…" He glanced at the two men on the floor. "Computer locates individuals with a cultural and hereditary tendency for having too many children and when that's combined with not being within standard-to-preferred social productivity scale, along with genetic markers for problematic—"

"It's all *moronic*!" Dino yelled, from the floor. "We are *artists*, and we are *productive* and we don't even *want* kids!"

The other one groaned. "Dino – I still can't move. Can you move yet?"

"Naw. Not from the neck down. We agreed, Shel. I volunteer. He can take me out."

Sheldon was sobbing. "That's bullshit, man. I didn't agree it was gonna be you."

Venter chewed his lower lip for a moment, then glanced at her apartment door number. He tapped on his pad, looking her up. "You're Sharon de los Santos?"

"Yes."

"You're her mother?"

"No." She looked at the floor. "I don't look like my picture anymore."

"You're a programmer. Or…coder of some kind. You work from home. You improve software. That's useful. That's…necessary."

"I'm a mask addict. I'm all about uChan. And who do I improve software for? Right – uChan! I'm…about half the age I look. I feel like…" It was hard to say.

But he seemed to understand. "You work. You pay into the economy. That's all we care about."

"I…haven't been getting much done. As little as I can."

He squinted his eyes, giving her a long silent look. Finally he said, "I only need one candidate. Rules say you can volunteer."

Boom – the car stopped at the sign. Road Ends. Beyond the sign was a rushing flood turned dark brown with dirt.

Sharon licked her dry lips. She flapped a hand toward the two young men on the floor. "You don't want to pick one of them. Am I right? You don't want to do it."

Venter shrugged. "I don't know. Hard to figure. The agency's got me on a…" He shook his head. "But still…it's okay with me if you want to do it."

"I really could? Volunteer?"

"You'd have to quit your job. With finality."

Her heart was picking up its pace. *Road Ends.*

She found herself turning, walking over to the console built into the wall. She tapped the number in and her boss appeared on the screen – a middle aged woman with thick eyebrows and bright orange lipstick. "Who the hell are *you*?"

"It's de los Santos. Sharon de los Santos."

The woman's eyes widened. "You look worse than I feel any Saturday morning."

"I'm quitting the job. I'm…" She heard the statement echo in her head as she spoke it, as if it were on some internal loudspeaker. "I'm done. I'm gone. I don't want to code another line. Tell them…"

She spent almost a full minute cussing them out.

Then she hit a button, making the woman's stunned face vanish.

Sharon turned back to Venter. "What else do I have to do?"

"Sign a form on my pad. Read the Social Context Statement in its entirety. Then you put your thumbprint on it next to your signature. Then – I put you down. Totally painless. You'll just go to sleep."

"And my body?"

"I got a special bag, compresses your tissues, dries it out, vents, your body weighs about twenty pounds after. Goes to an incinerator."

"I…" She was collapsing inside, like a building with rotten timbers. "Let's do it."

"You sure? Maybe want to change your mind?"

She shook her head. A great weight was slipping off her – as if she already weighed only twenty pounds. "I'm a waste. Just a waste." She took a deep breath. "I'm sure."

Venter turned to Sheldon and Dino. "You two, when the paralysis wears off, just go off and find something to do. Make yourself useful somewhere. People are starving to death. Billions of them. Be useful."

Then he turned to Sharon, pointed to his pad and said, "Sign right here."

5. CHARLIE VENTER

He was within fifty paces of the squid balloon when he was sure he needed to talk to Mei. He had to call her right away. If he didn't, he'd feel like he had so much weight on him the balloon wouldn't take off.

Part Three of the Social Context Statement kept going through his mind. He was hearing the woman's rusty voice reading it back to him: "Justice is rarely complete. We are aware of that. What is just for society is sometimes unjust for the individual. Resources must be conserved, so that the lives of those who are found to be within usefulness-scale parameters can be optimized. Hence this painless procedure. We respect your dignity as a human being and appreciate your cooperation. Your name will be added to the file of those who sacrificed…"

Sacrificed for fear. Venter knew something Ivy and Chou didn't know; something de los Santos hadn't known; that his job wasn't particularly about population control. That was just the shell of it. Underneath, it was about *motivation*. He wasn't allowed to tell anyone, not even Mei. But it was really about *Don't give up or the weedkiller will get you. Be productive or we'll come looking…*

It was an old idea, and it was sick, and it wasn't working, really, and it was…his job.

Even the slang *weedkiller* had been created by the agency, planted on social media. Truth was, most people who'd given up couldn't be found. But they might be…motivated.

Her hand was shaking when she put her thumbprint on the pad. But he remembered her face as she'd gone to sleep for the last time, lying on the unzipped body bag. She looked a little younger, when she drifted off, with a slight smile. Maybe that's what being at peace was really like.

Venter trudged on through close, muggy air; over rocks and broken walls. He was sticky with sweat when he got to the balloon. He saw that someone had tried to break into the cab, and it had defended itself. He stepped over the body, was recognized and the door opened for him.

He climbed up into the cab, and went to the pilot's seat. Then he called Mei. He left the video off.

Her voice was rich with dread. "What is it? You never call me from work…"

"I just…I made up my mind."

"What?"

"I'm a waste, Mei. In this job. I make a living but…I'm still a waste. I'm going to try to find something else. Some other way to be useful."

"So you're going to put Christine at risk. And me. You know it's almost impossible for you to find any other job that maintains you at this life-style." He could hear her furious breathing as she took it all in. "If you do it, I'm going to go stay with my dad. You might never see Christine again, Charlie."

"I know."

"Oh God. I know what it is! You haven't been taking your pills."

"I took the pill, Mei. But…sometimes they don't work. Sometimes I feel something anyway."

He broke the connection, released the anchors, and the squid balloon rose up, buoyantly up, into the air.

John Shirley's cyberpunk trilogy *A Song Called Youth* has been collected into one volume by Prime Books. His novels *City Come A-Walkin'* and *Demons* are still in print and his newest novel is *Doyle After Death* from HarperCollins.

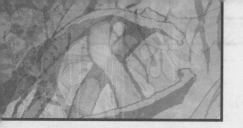

BLONDE PRIYA SHARMA

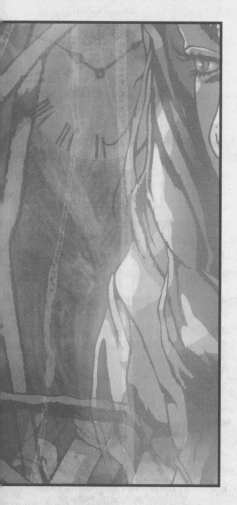

"When did you go bald?"

Only Clarice would ask such a forthright question.

"Leave her alone." Jake drains his beer. Only he would dare contradict his sister.

The clock hands have gone from late at night to early in the morning. Jake's bar is empty of customers. The staff, who are sitting round the table, fall silent, intent on their drinks.

"It's okay," Rapunzel says. "I was sick and it all fell out."

Her scalp is shiny, every follicle devoid of life. Nor does she have any eyebrows. Or hair elsewhere for that matter.

"What colour was it?"

"Blonde."

There's a pause, then laughter.

Jake nudges her. "You're a joker after all."

She knows what he thinks of her. That she's vague and evasive and hasn't a clue what's going on most of the time.

"Lucky you're beautiful enough to be bald," he adds.

Rapunzel touches the nape of her neck where she feels most exposed and tries not to smile.

ART BY MARTIN HANFORD

Rapunzel brushes her hair. One hundred strokes to make it gleam. It's easiest at night after her haircut, when it only reaches her neck. Static made it float.

Morning brushing's a chore that makes her arm ache as her hair reaches to her knees. One hundred stokes and it falls like a sheet of silk.

"Real blonde hair." Matilda touches it as though she still can't believe it. "Women in the city use dye to get this colour but the chemicals turn their hair to straw."

Rapunzel's heard this a million times before. Natural blondes are on the brink of extinction. Redheads only exist in far flung corners of the world where people live in tribes.

"They'll kill you out there if they ever see this. They'll tear your hair out from the roots." Rapunzel's heard this before too. "Don't be scared, my angel. I'll always be here to protect you."

....

The warehouses are in a seedy part of the city that's been lifted by association with the rich bohemian crowd in the neighbouring district. The warehouses that were once used as doss houses are now bars, artists' co-operatives and thrift stores. The old seamen's church is a sex shop. A few drug dealers still hang around to provide both rich and poor a fix.

It's not entirely safe but it's better than it used to be. To stray too far from the busier streets is to risk a kicking. It gives the privileged a frisson of fear that they find delicious.

Rapunzel knows that all the punters in Jake's bar look at her. She mimics Clarice's toughness, missing their second glance. She's attractive. Isn't everyone, if only we learn how to use our eyes?

Rapunzel likes playing the piano best, but like all the staff she does everything from cleaning toilets to table service. Tonight she's on the bar. Clarice presents her tray.

"Six beers for the posh boys in the booth."

A young man gets up from this group and comes over. He's shy away from his friends. They all dress down in a uniform of torn T-shirts and roughly chopped fringes, worn slightly too long.

"You slumming it, then?"

He flushes. Clarice is democratic with her insults. To his credit, he's not put off. Rapunzel lays

out the bottles on the tray and Clarice whisks it away.

"My name's Adam." He flicks his fringe out of his eyes. "What's your name?"

"Rapunzel." She says it under her breath, like it's a line she's been practising.

"I've heard you play the piano. You're good. Where did you study?"

"Nowhere." She busies herself, wiping down the bar. "I just had a lot of time to practise."

Clarice comes back with her tray under her arm. "Is Prince Charming here bothering you?"

....

Rapunzel lives in a suite of rooms in the mansion's turret. Its windows are covered in metal lattices whose delicacy belie their strength. The door to the suite opens at the same time each day.

"Morning."

Rapunzel, still in her nightgown, gets up and stretches. Matilda puts down the tray, goes back to the door to lock it and then pockets the key.

"Why do you do that?"

"What?"

"Lock us in."

"I've told you lots of times. Safety. Suppose someone crept in while we were having breakfast? Now, we have fruit, toast and a special treat."

"Wouldn't it be safer if I was downstairs with you? I could help keep watch."

Matilda lays out their repast. "A good idea but it'd be dangerous if someone saw you."

"I could wear a headscarf."

"There's the beast to consider too."

"Beast?"

"I've trained a huge hound. It only obeys me. I can't risk it attacking you by mistake."

"But…"

"It's the safest way. It'll protect you when I'm not here. Come and eat."

The platter's pattern is concealed by white fans of sliced apple and bright strawberries. The toast's served in an antique rack and the butter in curls. The treat's hot chocolate, so thick that the silver teaspoons stand up in it.

"Don't forget your hair tonic."

It's a bitter concoction to aid hair health that Matilda brews with herbs from the garden.

Breakfast always ends the same way, Matilda clearing everything away and then locking Rapunzel in.

. . . .

Alone in the tower, Rapunzel's day is punctuated by markers. Cleaning, bathing, trimming her profuse body hair, an hour of piano practice, sketching and reading. She longs for Matilda's company.

"Play for me." Tired from a day in the vegetable garden, Matilda throws herself down in an armchair. She's washed her hands and face, but Rapunzel pulls the leaves from Matilda's fringe, humming. "Play me something nice."

Matilda wasn't the most patient teacher but Rapunzel has had lots of time to practise. She knows all her sheet music by heart now, plus all the variations she's composed. She picks a soothing tune and Matilda closes her eyes.

"My mother used to play that to us." Her smile makes Rapunzel think it's a treasured memory. The smile falters. "It'd break her heart to see this place now. There used to be servants and dances. People working the land."

"What happened?"

"War. It tore through everything." Her mouth turns down. "They hung my father from the gatehouse arch. I remember how the horses screamed as they were hacked to death."

Matilda's eyes snap open, as if she's woken from a nightmare. "Enough of that. Time for your haircut."

Matilda pulls the scissors from her apron pocket that contains multitudes. She inspects Rapunzel's scalp and combs out her locks, looking for split ends. She binds it at the nape of Rapunzel's neck, and then again a fraction lower, and cuts between the two to lift away the golden rope. Her eyes are bright with desire.

Hair has a life cycle. Rapunzel's is in a permanent, rapid anagen phase. Abnormally fast growth that means by morning it's long again.

. . . .

They stick together at Jake's. Rapunzel envies the other girls' robustness. She feels fragile and vulnerable by comparison. She starts lifting crates of bottles to try and build up her strength.

One night someone tries to rob them while they're locking up. Peter comes out of the kitchen at first shout, swinging a meat cleaver. Jake goes for a pair of long knives that he keeps under the bar. The bouncers pull out axes. Clarice smashes the end from a bottle, beer spraying everywhere.

It's complete overkill. It's a stringy junkie chancing his arm but Rapunzel feels anger swelling up inside her. She doesn't recognise it at first. It overrides thought and sense. She tackles him with an arm around his legs, which wouldn't be very effective if he wasn't high. She's on her feet before he is. There's a crack as one of his ribs gives way under her boot. She can't stop herself. She's furious that someone can threaten all that she considers hers. She's furious that's she spent most of her life in a room playing the piano and washing her hair without questioning why. She's furious at Matilda. She keeps on kicking until Peter lifts her away.

Jake squats beside him. "Listen, you little fucker, come in here again and I'll let her have you."

Rapunzel realises that Jake means her. The bouncers carry the man out to dump him at a distance.

Jake takes her aside. "You need to learn how to throw a punch and how to take one. Clarice can teach you."

Adrenaline makes her bold. "No. You."

. . . .

Matilda puts a plate of stew down in front of her.

"Thank you, Mother."

"Whatever made you say that?"

"I just thought…" Rapunzel shifts in her seat. "I mean, you talked about your mother. In my books there are mothers. Aren't you mine?"

Matilda sits down. Rapunzel's not sure if she's angry or not.

"I didn't give birth to you, if that's what you mean." She sounds stiff and defensive. "I'm the one who looks after you. I feed you. I care for you when you're sick. I cut your hair. Isn't that what a mother is?"

Rapunzel opens her mouth, then shuts it. Matilda's not like the rosy cheeked, plump mothers in the illustrations. She's tall and strong. Her fierceness over Rapunzel's protection is absolute.

"Don't you love me?" Matilda starts to cry.

Surprised by this reaction, so does Rapunzel. "I love you. Of course I do. I'm sorry."

"Your mother didn't want you." That makes

Rapunzel flinch. Matilda softens it with, "I wanted you. I delivered you. I blew into your mouth to get you breathing. I was the first to hold you. You were covered in long blonde hairs. My little hairball."

Her mother's role in the event has been diminished.

"What was she like?"

Her persistence makes Matilda frown but she answers the question.

"Dirt poor and drugged up. I'm not sure how she found her way this far. She got into the garden before I'd finished repairing the wall. She was eating my lamb's lettuce."

When Rapunzel stands on a chair she can see the garden from her window; the vegetable plot, the orchard and then the wall.

"I could help you in the garden. Or with the chickens," Rapunzel says hopefully, even though she knows what the answer will be.

. . . .

apunzel's sat at her desk, loose hair draped over her shoulders like a cape, sketching Matilda from memory. She clutches her pencil like it's a weapon when the door swings open. It's far too early in the afternoon for Matilda to visit.

It's a young man. Full lipped with short, brown hair. His clothes are faded and shabby. He doesn't look like a prince. More like a handsome, undernourished wolf.

"Have you come to rape and kill me?"

"No!" He holds up both hands, dropping the pillow case he's carrying. Rapunzel recognises the embroidered monogram as Matilda's. The silver cutlery within spills out. "Sorry," he adds, like a guilty child.

"The door was locked. How did you get in?"

"It's a skill. My dad used to say I had keys instead of fingernails." He waves his fingers as if demonstrating this peculiarity. "I won't hurt you. I promise. And I'll put all these back."

"Matilda will be angry if you don't."

"Tall woman? She's gone out. I watched her ride off." He reaches for her hair. "Is it real?"

Rapunzel's mute, frightened to admit it, even though the evidence is on her head. He gently tugs at a strand which comes away.

"Ouch."

"Sorry." He holds the gold filament up the light.

"It *is* real. I've never seen hair this colour before. Not natural, except on a wig once."

Rapunzel's equally fascinated. She's never seen a man before. The men in Rapunzel's books are creatures to fall in love with. As mythical as unicorns, Matilda said. They're not like that anymore. They're all monsters.

"Are you a prisoner? Why are you locked up?"

"I live here."

"Who with?"

"Just Matilda." She holds up her sketch. "You can meet her." *She'll see that not all men are monsters after all.*

"I don't think that's such a good idea. What's your name?"

"Rapunzel."

"I'm Billy."

She pours him a glass of water and gives him an apple.

"Your hair's the colour of chocolate." The idea makes Rapunzel smile.

"Chocolate?" he laughs. "That's only for rich people."

Am I rich? Rapunzel thinks.

"Here." She opens the drawer and takes out a tiny parcel, tied with string. "Take it."

He unwraps the paper to find a square of chocolate inside. She savours the moment when his lips part and he puts it in his mouth. His eyelids flutter with the shock of such sweetness. A dimple appears in his cheek.

"I should go. Before your friend comes back."

"Will you come back and see me?"

"Do you want me to? I'd like that but you have to promise me you won't tell."

. . . .

apunzel's never had a secret before. Waiting for Billy makes the days longer.

"Be careful of the beast."

"What?"

"A hound that Matilda's trained to attack."

"I've never seen an animal in here."

She leans over and pulls a bramble from his hair. They both laugh. His confidence diminishes her fear.

"I've been sleeping under hedgerows outside the walls, waiting for Matilda to leave."

"Where does she go?"

"Towards the city."

Rapunzel puts the bramble in a pewter dish. Billy wanders around the room.

"It's so beautiful here. Peaceful. What are these for?"

"They're grape scissors," she explains as he inspects the ornate handles. "For cutting grapes with."

"What are grapes?"

"I don't know."

He looks at everything. The paintings and the tapestries, the books, even though he can't read. The porcelain fascinates him the most. He holds up a teacup that's so fine it glows translucent in the light.

"It's so delicate."

The way he says it makes her want to cry. His soul craves beauty.

"I used to talk to them."

His look is a question.

"The cups. The pictures. Matilda says they're precious. I talked to them when I felt lonely."

"Talk to me."

They talk all afternoon. He tells her about the city. The alleyways where he grew up, the riches and poverty. Rapunzel doesn't mention the haircuts and keeps her hair bound in a loose net so that Billy can't see it growing. She's not ready for that yet.

"Come away with me."

"I can't. I can't leave."

Matilda's lied to her. Billy isn't a hairy rampaging brute. He reaches out for her hand.

"Come outside then. Just for a little while. Come and stand beneath the trees. They're lovely."

"I can't." *I'm afraid.*

Rapunzel's never left her rooms.

．．

The staff at Jake's live in. Frank and John (twins and bouncers) and Peter (cook) have the first floor. Jake sleeps in his office behind the bar. The second floor belongs to the women – Clarice, Sienna, Marta, Mary and Rapunzel. The long rooms once stored sacks of grain but now there are rows of beds. Doors are hinged together to make a folding screen when privacy's required. When Rapunzel's talent for painting is discovered they make her decorate the walls, great murals of fantastic animals from her memory of the picture books she grew up with. Uni-

corns, griffins and lions that earn her a burst of applause.

Everything's up for grabs. Marta emerges with a shirt that Sienna made, wearing it as a dress. There'll be a spat over a necklace or a set of bangles but it never lasts long.

Rapunzel loves the communality. Of waking to the sounds of others' breathing, footsteps, farts and laughter. Best of all, here a cup is just a cup. Rough-hewn and functional. Objects have their rightful place. How utterly proper.

．．

"Are you eating, poppet?"

"Yes, why?"

"You look like you're losing weight. Are you eating all the food you're saving for snacks?"

When Rapunzel refused food as a child, Matilda would slap her legs. *After the war we starved. I'll never starve again. You'll not leave a morsel, do you hear?*

"Yes, I eat everything."

She's been saving the food for Billy. She thinks of him, huddled under a bush somewhere. At least she can give him something to eat for the days he's got to wait to see her.

Rapunzel sits at the piano and plays. She doesn't see Matilda pick up the pewter bowl, frowning when she sees the dried bramble in it.

．．

"I've seen hair your colour in the city wigmaker's. They're very expensive."

"Really?"

"Rapunzel…" Billy pauses. "Will you let your hair down?"

Billy's request makes her feel shy, as if he's asking her to take her clothes off. She wants to, though. She undoes the hair net and takes out the clips, like a queen removing her crown. He puts his hands in it, so it spills through his fingers, then buries his face in it.

She can't remember who kissed whom first. Kissing is a revelation. She pulls his shirt over his head. He unbuttons her dress.

"I don't know what to do. Show me."

He puts his fingers between her legs, as his mouth covers hers. She pushes him off and kneels over him, examining him as much as he examines her. It hurts, taking him in, but it's nice too.

Rapunzel lies facing him, their arms draped over one another. She strokes his skin. Their breathing slows. Sleep comes to the sated. Neither of them hear the door open. Matilda's oiled the lock and hinges.

Rapunzel wakes with a start. Her face is wet and she wipes it, wondering why she's been crying in her sleep. Her palm is red.

The axe bites again, deep into Billy's head and neck. His arms flail, a useless reflex. Rapunzel's heels kick against the floorboards. His wound is spraying blood in ever weakening arcs. His body jerks and shakes, then settles into dead stillness.

"What did he do to you?" Matilda shakes her by the shoulders. "What did you let him do?"

Matilda looms over her, blood-splattered and panting. Rapunzel tries to cover herself. Matilda's seen her naked before, having bathed her as a child. She's not a child anymore. She can't stop shaking. She doesn't realise that she's rocking, arms around herself, or that she's sitting in a puddle of her own urine. All she can do is stare as Matilda wraps Billy in a sheet and drags him from the room.

When she finally finds her feet, she stands on a chair and looks out to where Matilda's burying Billy under the lovely trees.

....

Rapunzel remembers sex. She lies in the quiet nights, scar itching, listening to assignations arranged for when everyone should be asleep. There are quick gasps and low moans. If you want to be noisy, find somewhere else.

She remembers how ridiculous and magnificent sex is. That such moments are meant to be fleeting or else she'd be paralysed forever, driven to madness if they remained so vivid.

She wants to have sex with Jake. To push him down, to lie with him, to feel it all again. Her want is born from a knowledge that's given her new eyes. She imagines his long fingers on her. When he taught her to fight, the tension and concentration in him when he dropped into a fighting stance made her shiver. His topknot and beard makes him look older and he treats all the staff like family when they've earned his trust.

This desire makes her feel guilty and she questions what she felt for Billy. She's ashamed that she doesn't know if she loved him or not. And the one person she knows she loved is Matilda, the woman who killed him.

....

Four months of silence follows. What was once between them is broken. Rapunzel refuses to get out of bed, turning her face to the wall. She defaces the paintings, smashes the porcelain and bends the tines of the pastry forks. Matilda looks at the defaced relics of her past and weeps.

When Matilda drags her to the table, Rapunzel refuses to eat. She refuses to wash her hair, which has become matted and tangled. Matilda beats her and then throws her in the tin bath, which gets tipped over in the struggle.

"Do you want us to starve?" Matilda cries. "Is that it?"

Rapunzel loses weight. Her cotton dresses, once snug on the arms, are now loose, but strangely the same dresses are tight around her middle.

One afternoon she falls asleep wearing a thin cotton nightgown. It's a hot, muggy day. She's woken by a gentle hand on her shoulder. Matilda's sitting on the edge of her bed.

"Your periods have stopped, haven't they?"

"Yes." Rapunzel eyes her with suspicion, wondering what that means.

"You're pregnant." Matilda's face softens. "You're going to have a baby."

Billy's baby. Her baby. She doesn't know if her heartbeat's propelled by fear or elation. She's glad she's lying down because her legs feel like water.

"Don't be scared." Matilda strokes her hair. "I'll look after you both. We'll put all this behind us. You'll have the best of everything. I'll bring the crib down from the attic. We'll make baby clothes together."

Matilda puts an arm around her.

"Child-rearing's difficult. You were such a fussy child, up all night worrying at the breast." She finishes with, "I wonder if the baby will be blonde?"

....

Rapunzel only realises how much she's been chewing and sucking on her hair when she tries to stop. She's teasing out the knots with a comb when Matilda comes in. The woman glances at her, but Rapunzel doesn't smile. *Go slowly. She has to believe you.*

She puts the comb down.

"I'll never forgive you for what you did but it's not about us anymore. I need you. You need me. It's us against the world. I want a safe life for my child."

Matilda has the grace to look chastised.

Rapunzel gobbles up the creamy porridge that Matilda's brought her. There's an amber pool of honey floating in it.

"I'm hungry. Bring me another. And the sewing basket. We're going to have to let my clothes out."

The door stays locked despite the newly forged truce.

Rapunzel gorges over the following months while she plans. She has to sit on her hands to stop the compulsive hair-pulling. It grows in thick, unruly waves.

One night, when Matilda comes up for her nightly cut, Rapunzel's waiting behind the door. She hits Matilda with a marble paperweight. The woman falls to her knees and Rapunzel hits her again, at the base of the neck. She pitches forward. Rapunzel kneels beside her. She's still breathing.

Rapunzel rolls her onto her side and fishes out the scissors from her apron pocket. The keys are where she dropped them. She fumbles and shakes, afraid that Matilda will wake up at any moment.

She's stitched a sack from one of her old dresses and filled it with whatever she thinks is of value that she hasn't destroyed. All she has to go on is Billy's wonderment, so there's a set of miniature mechanical toys, silk handkerchiefs, a pearl necklace and a painted fan. Also, some chocolate and apples.

Then she steps outside the chambers that have contained her for the last sixteen years. There's no time to consider it. She locks Matilda in and then she does something she's never done before. She cuts her own hair, as short as she can. She covers the clumsy tufts with a scarf and pockets the scissors. She'll need them to keep her hair short so she can cover it.

"Rapunzel." There's a low moan from the other side of the door. "Let me out."

Rapunzel freezes. She holds a breath. A reflex.

"Help me. Please. I'm hurt. I'm bleeding."

Rapunzel covers her mouth with both hands. She hadn't expected it to feel like this. The door handle rattles.

"I know you're there. Open the door."

A sob escapes from Rapunzel's lips.

"Open the door—" Matilda sounds sharper "—and I'll forgive you."

The door shakes under Matilda's hammering fist.

"Let me out, you ungrateful bitch. The hound will find you. It'll rip your throat out."

Rapunzel shrinks back from the sudden venom.

"I'm sorry. I didn't mean it. Let me out. I'll die in here otherwise."

Rapunzel's legs quiver as Matilda's voice follows her down the corridor.

"You might think that boy of yours was nice but you won't survive out there. They're wolves, every single one."

Matilda howls. She sounds, Rapunzel thinks, like a beast – uncomprehending and wounded at her betrayal.

The rest of the house might as well be a foreign country. It's a silent, grand hovel. Light filters through grimy windows and the carpets are worn through. The furniture is a feast for woodworms, the silk wallpaper stained by archaic floods, the pattern lost to mould.

It's clear that Matilda has kept her most precious things in the tower.

Rapunzel doesn't linger. She follows the grand sweeping bannister downwards, treading lightly, brandishing the scissors in case the beast attacks. The kitchen is at the back of the house. The fire's burning low. Beside it is a straw pallet covered in blankets. The worktops are clear but the kitchen tablet is piled with junk. Rapunzel goes through the larder, taking a ham and a loaf.

Then she sees the heavy manacles fixed to the kitchen's far wall. Their height from the floor suggests a sizeable beast. Rapunzel fumbles with the keys, trying one, dropping the bunch, retrieving it and then trying another, all the time imagining some giant, vicious dog. She opens it and darts into the yard.

The bright day floors her. She's unprepared for

the world in more ways than one. She crumples under its vastness. Her heart works double time. She gets to her feet, despite the dizziness.

She remembers what Billy told her about the way out; through Matilda's immaculate garden with its rows of lettuces, courgettes and raspberry canes. She heads for the trees, stopping at the plot where the grass has started to grow back. She looks up through the lattice of branches. Billy was right, she thinks, the trees are lovely. She's glad he has this view.

After a thorny negotiation with the brambles, Rapunzel finds the hole in the wall. It doesn't occur to her to go through the main gate. She has the keys. Nor does it occur to her to stay.

....

One of Clarice's friends comes into the bar. They sit together in a corner, the woman holding a baby to her full breast. The child searches for her nipple with its rosebud mouth, sucking vigorously when it latches on. A mother, equipped to feed her child. Rapunzel's understanding is instinctive. The body prepares itself.

Matilda's words come back to her like a bolt. The clues assemble themselves. She curses herself as an idiot.

You were such a fussy feeder, up all night worrying at the breast.

The iron collar and chains in the kitchen. There'd never been a hound, just a woman that Matilda had treated like an animal. Was her mother buried near Billy, beneath the trees?

....

It's a long walk under an open sky which presses down on her when she dares to look up at it. She wishes for boots like Matilda's when her feet blister and bleed. She shelters under bushes by night, pulling her shawl around her.

Finally she sees an unnatural skyline. The expanse of city comes to her in growing detail; the outline of towers, sunlight flashing on a row of windows.

The abdominal pains start as she passes under the great arch. She's ignored the grumbling but now it's a rising colic. So it is that she arrives, between a shiver and a sweat, clutching her stomach.

Pain makes mincemeat of her. Sweat runs from her face and drops from her chin. She's on her knees, trying not to cry out. People crowd around her. Someone puts a hand on her shoulder and lifts off the woollen shawl. Light fingers relieve her of her makeshift bag.

"Matilda," she says, a reflex, and then she blacks out.

....

The world returns to Rapunzel in fleeting pieces. First bright lights and then a masked face. When she tries to sit up, she's pushed back down, firmly but gently. She's tethered by tubes in her arm, from her abdomen and between her legs.

A man's face looms into view. He pulls down the paper mask to reveal a crooked grin. "Hello, sweetie." The smile widens. "What's your name?"

"Rapunzel."

"Never heard that one before."

She reaches up to her face. She has a mask on too.

"Leave that on. It's oxygen."

"Oxygen?"

"Just breathe it in, darling, breathe it in."

....

When she next wakes, Rapunzel feels like she's floating and her mouth is dry. The tube going into her arm carries red fluid from a flabby bag on a stand. She turns her head to see a woman beside her, writing in a file. Her skin's black, a contrast to the vivid green of her dress. In her stupor, Rapunzel thinks, *Beautiful.*

"Is that blood?"

The woman's head jerks up. She's much older than Rapunzel first thought.

"Yes, to replace some of what you lost." She puts her pen in the top pocket of the dress. "I'm Doctor Ellard, your surgeon. I've come to talk to you about the operation."

"Operation?"

"Yes, you're in Seven Sisters' Hospital. My colleague over at the Mission Clinic called me and asked me if I'd see you as you'd been taken there after you collapsed. You're very fortunate. If I hadn't owed him a favour, you'd be dead now."

Rapunzel lifts her sheet. She's a mass of dressings. The tube from between her legs carries urine into a bag on a stand. The one from her abdomen is more shocking, having breached the integrity of her skin, carrying pus and blood from the unnatural orifice to yet another bag.

"Are you in pain?"

Rapunzel nods.

"I'll get the nurse to bring you something."

"What about my baby?"

Rapunzel guesses that Dr Ellard isn't surprised very often because she struggles to hide it.

"You thought you were pregnant?"

"Yes, my periods stopped. My belly swelled."

Dr Ellard shakes her head. A tear rolls down Rapunzel's cheek.

"I'm sorry." The surgeon touches her arm. "You definitely weren't pregnant."

"No baby?"

"No. You've been chewing your hair, haven't you? We removed a giant hairball from your stomach. A trichobezoar. The tail end went into your small intestine. It nearly killed you."

Rapunzel only registers several words. Hairball. Stomach. Killed.

"Rapunzel, there's one other thing."

What else could there possibly be?

....

Alopecia totalis. Rapunzel's body, shocked and insulted by illness and intervention, has shed every single hair.

The abdominal drain, the catheter and drip are disconnected. Rapunzel, untethered, is free to roam the ward. She stands in the communal bathroom once the other women are in bed and looks at her broken image in the cracked mirror.

Her armpits are smooth caverns. There are no eyebrows to frame her face. The lack of pubic hair makes her feel childish and shy. She puts her hand to her shiny, vulnerable scalp.

Rapunzel peels back her dressing to look at her long scar. It's an angry, heaped up ridge. It doesn't matter that it's ugly. That's only vanity. She puts her hands on her flat abdomen. She's been emptied of everything.

....

The man's ten minutes late for their appointment. He stoops to hide his height, which makes him looks older.

"I'm Jimmy. I work for Social Care. I've been assigned to you."

"Social Care?"

"I work with people who are about to leave hospital but still need help."

"Oh." She's not thought about what'll happen next.

"Where are you from, Rapunzel? Do you have family I can contact?"

She shakes her head.

"That's okay. The nurses say you like to read. I've bought some things to look at. You must get bored in here."

Jimmy pulls some newspapers from his bag and starts to flick through them, pointing at things and chatting to her about them. They're not like her beautiful books. The paper's coarse and the print's ugly. He puts her at her ease though. After about twenty minutes he surprises her with, "You're not from here are you? I think you've not been around many people at all."

She's not sure if she's unhappy or grateful that this gawky, bowed man has observed her every reaction to his chatter and divined her with a few seemingly casual questions. He hasn't once opened the file with her name on it, like everyone else does. He's read it all and remembered.

"Who's been looking after you all these years?"

She shakes her head. He nods in response, respecting her silence.

"Rapunzel, I've got to ask you this, and if you'd rather speak to a woman I'll try and find you one." He clears his throat. "You thought you were pregnant. Has anyone hurt you?"

"No." It comes out more forcefully than she intends. It's only later that she ponders notions of hurt.

They lapse into silence. She likes that he doesn't gabble and gives her a chance to speak, but when she doesn't, he says, "You're a celebrity. Doctor Ellard's persuaded the hospital board to waive the fee for all your care. Most people would've been out on the street by now."

There had been a different kind of fee. Dr Ellard had taken her to the hospital lecture hall on several occasions. Rapunzel had been a live specimen, her pickled hairball beside her. She couldn't bear to look at it, imagining it growing inside her. The doctors all commented on her being a natural blonde. At the end of the first session, Dr Ellard stood up and said, *I intend to call this phenomenon Rapunzel Syndrome.*

"Yes, Doctor Ellard's been kind to me."

"There's something else we need to talk about.

You're due for discharge soon. I've applied for a place at a charity safe house for a few months. They'll teach you some of what you need to learn to survive. What can you do?"

"Play piano. Paint. I want to work. To look after myself."

"Good, because there's no other choice."

....

I t's harder to sit alone in a room now that Rapunzel knows there's a teeming world outside. The room at The Sisters of the Melancholic Heart is a plain white cell with a bed.

"I'm sorry." Jimmy's shrug is apologetic and weary. "It's the best I could find."

She learns quickly, of money, of cooking. The food is terrible. There are regular power cuts and candles are precious. She starts helping the staff with the motley collection in their care; a woman with a jagged scar across her forehead (a victim of assault), a man picking at imagined creatures on his skin, another who's had both legs amputated. At first she's scared by these unmanned souls.

Jimmy drops in when he can. He brings her a map with the no-go areas marked in red.

"You need to start going out. Look for work. You've not much time left. The staff at the hospital have had a whip-round. There's enough for a few weeks rent. I can help you find somewhere."

So much for Matilda's savage world.

Rapunzel finds the sheer number of people that she sees on the street staggering, as well as their plethora of sizes, colours and shapes. In her books all she saw were pale princesses and manly princes.

The city itself is a revelation. From its towers to its tenements. She looks at dresses in shop windows on the grand avenues before she's moved on. There's the smell of frying onions from a cart. Sewerage from an open drain. She goes into a church, lured by a choir who clap and sway, but she struggles with the concept of God. The sound contrasts with the crowd that gathers to watch a fistfight.

One day she ventures into the crafts quarter, where the skilled and handy ply their trade. There's a sign that says CITY WIGMAKER. It has a small window, covered by bars. Rapunzel stands, open mouthed. A single wig is on display. It's long and blonde, falling in waves. People stop and look at it. She waits until she's alone and then rings the bell. She keeps on ringing until she hears footsteps. The grille in the door snaps open and an annoyed face looks out.

"Appointment only. What do you want?"

"I want to see the wig." She points towards the window.

"No chance." The man snickers. "You look like you need one though. Go to Marling Street. You might be able to afford them. They cut hair from corpses, cheap bastards."

"I want to look at that one."

"You can't afford it. It's pure, natural blonde. I don't want your sort here. Piss off."

"Where did you get the hair? Matilda?" It's been such a long time since she's said the name aloud.

"You know Matilda?" His face is transformed. "Where has she been? Do you know how to find her?"

So, her curse had been a wigmaker's dream. How he must've rubbed his hands when Matilda opened her bag. Rapunzel, the goose, forever laying golden eggs.

The wigmaker flings the door open but it's too late. Rapunzel's covered her head and has mingled with the crowd. His voice follows her up the street.

"Can you get a message to Matilda? Please, come back. You can try the wig on. Just tell Matilda I need more hair!"

....

R apunzel passes an open warehouse door in the old shipping district. The tables are made from packing crates and the chairs are mismatched. There's a man behind the bar putting bottles on the shelves. His black hair is swept up in a topknot and he has a beard. He looks up and sees her, tilting his head. That decides her. She goes in.

"I need a job."

Loud, harsh laughter makes her turn around. Rapunzel missed the woman sweeping the floor.

"Clarice," the man growls.

Rapunzel can't stop staring at Clarice's hair. Blue-black and cut into fearsome spikes around her face, with a heavy fringe.

"What are you looking at?" the woman snarls.

"Your hair. It's beautiful."

Rapunzel catches sight of her own reflection in the mirror behind the bar. The mixture of innocence and stupidity makes her blush.

Clarice throws down her mop and goes through the door at the back.

"Fuck, I thought I was going to have to get between you. My sister's a firecracker. Hey, I'm Jake. What can you do?"

"I can play that." Rapunzel points to the up-right piano.

"It's junk. I keep meaning to chop it up for firewood."

She lifts the lid and touches a key. It makes a sour note.

"I can tune this."

She runs her fingers along the keyboard, demonstrating her skill.

"What's your name?"

"Rapunzel."

Clarice comes out, carrying a plate which she puts down in front of Rapunzel.

"You look hungry. Eat this, sweetie."

"She can play the piano." Jake raises an eyebrow at Clarice.

"She's adorable. I think we should keep her."

"Hey, your hair's growing back." It's Jake that notices first.

It comes in as a slow creeping stubble that begins as a dark fuzz. Rapunzel likes to run her hand over it, the blunt ends tickling her palm. Oh, the myth of sensuality and long hair. Rapunzel likes it short. It makes her feel strong.

The best bit is the colour. A glorious shade of mousey brown.

Rapunzel Syndrome is a rare condition in which trichophagia (eating hair) results in the formation of a trichobezoar (a hairball) in the stomach and its tail extends into the small intestine. As hair can't be digested, this in turn can cause malnutrition, weight loss, abdominal pain, bowel obstruction and perforation. Priya Sharma's stories have appeared in previous issues of *Interzone* as well as our sister magazine *Black Static*, and have been reprinted in various year's best anthologies. She also has a new story available on Tor.com called 'Fabulous Beasts'. More info can be found at priyasharmaficton.wordpress.com.

art by DAVE SENECAL

NO REZ JEFF NOON

His speculative fiction pieces stretch and play with...

into darkness

Waking the same every morning,
The darkness of the eye
Waiting for the day to kick in, the first little

pixel

Now, there it shines, now more of them, little squares of green light forming numbers 7:15 clock now orange now yellow, white, red four pixels per square inch, now eight, sixteen, thirty-two onwards, casting sleep away, my world gathering itself in my vision: oh my precious little squares and cubes of light and colour, collecting yourselves, making the room glow in my sight. Blink...

> BANK WITH US, ALL SAFE & SECURE. LOW RATES FOR LOW REZZERS

Bloody hell, first pop-up, barely awake. It's always the money grabbing bastards that hit you from the get go, bastards blink it away, wish I could

Up. Dressed. Grunt to Tom as he comes out of the bathroom pale flesh blurred (thank god) Dream? Did I? Yes of what? Strange, don't usually dream. Too few pixels it seems in the mind, infecting, or so they say:

As you see the world, so you think about the world

> DON'T SUFFER UGLINESS IN YOUR EYES. GOLDEN GLOW WORLD VISION. THE WORLD'S BEST FILTERING SYSTEM. **DEMO** AVAILABLE

Yes, grab that **demo**. A five second burst of Hi-Rez. Save for later, stash it with the others. Nice little collection now, and maybe, see Katie sometime, use it then. Maybe?

Out now. Biking it. Glory. Extra pixels kicking in courtesy of the company's upgrade. Here I am, riding the streets, dragging the world into my seven cameras, stealing the world, streaming it down to HQ and then out to the big server hubs, offshore, or out in the edgelands, I've heard, giant concrete slabs filled with machines, blinking lights. Stories I've heard, just a couple of people attending as the nation's collected info streams and surges and bubbles and fires off at tangents ever circling in the web, the warp and weft of our lives, here now, me zooming the streets aboard my pixel bike, I am the seeker of of of life! Fuck, good buzz in the head, just like those games I used to play, first person shoot-em-ups, crazy, just like that, the world blistering before me in light and colours and sheets of noise [***] Wooh nea rly, then ! A red car crackling at ragged edge of vis ion, a sudden cut-out to black, what? Fu ck Why I wonder ? Nearly crashed.

> REMEMBER, GOOD CITIZENS: YOU ARE WHAT YOU SEE

Need to... Fuck. Scary. Just keep riding, riding. Need to talk to Bella about it, tech geek: strange life she has, in her tiny dark room, drinking booze all day, her talk of finding some hyper pixel shit one day and all that weird stuff she builds... Oh coming back now... yes, can see OK now yes, better now. A little. Back to normal, gathering the city back into my lenses, as I ride, swerving through the cars like no other rider, ever, watch me world!

> STREAM FEED: TODAY IN PARLIAMENT, NEW HIGHER RESOLUTION LAWS TO BE DISCUSSED...

On. City, I will be your eyes today, I will glorify you in the stream, continuously, all your myriad pixels firing as one.

> REBELS CONFIDENT THEY CAN RECLAIM A DEGREE OF PRIVACY FOR THE PUBLIC. BUT THE CORPORATE LOBBY...

So many vision-pops today. Wish I could afford better, cleaner worldview. OK. Control. Ride it easy.

> ...PUSHING FOR EXTRA PIXELS TO BE RELEASED INTO REALITY

Once we were hunters, then gatherers. Then workers. Then service providers. Now streamers, surfers, users, blip seekers. Pixel chasers, image junkies, hyper reality buffs, dreamers. Seekers of the golden resolution, the view that gives you life complete, as beauty only, pure, filtered clean of all pain, all ugliness, all suffering and doubt. Oh glory, imagine!

> HERE IS TODAY'S PIXEL COUNT, ISSUED BY THE MET OFFICE AT 8:00...

I am my POV, nothing more

> HAZE IN PLACES, THEN GOOD RESOLUTION COVERAGE LATER. THERE MAY BE SOME CRUMBLE AT THE EDGES IN THE SOUTH. SO BE ALERT ALL YOU LOW-REZZERS OUT THERE

Morning shift done, back to HQ. Off the clock   Pixels dropping away from my vision as I park the bike...   No waste,   not from English Eye, nation's number one reality stream,   updating   on the second, every second!   real time.

Canteen. There she is...   Katie. Isn't it?   Difficult, sometimes to tell, when just off the bike, adjusting to the lower rez level. Snazzy. She always get the best streams...   Rides a mean machine, gathers more reality than any of us.   Might ask her out,   maybe   Should do, yes.   Use all my   collected demos up in one amazing night, imagine...

> RESOLUTION IS MONEY! BE IMAGE RICH, TODAY. YOU DESERVE IT

Yes Touching her flesh,   imagine   and her eyes, seeing my face, clear,

full of beauty, me imagine. Yes, share the demos (have about twelve saved up) Mutual vision: two POVs seeing the   glory in each other, imagine, life,   as it could be lived

Orgasm jeez imagine: All twelve demos taken   at once   Whoosh! Blossom.

Shit, she's uh what? Christ   she's talking to me... Her words, halfway broken as mine... probably shares my rez level, sweet, best that way, everyone says so: stick to your own rez level, because...   Nobody wants to to imagine another person seeing them   as ugly. Christ, no

> WARNING. THIS IS YOUR WORLDVIEW PROVIDER. WE ARE CURRENTLY EXPERIENCING FLUCTUATIONS IN THE SECONDARY REALITY LAYERS

Lips, move yourselves, answer her: Sure, yes, absolutely (not actually saying anything, not at all) But see, in the haze of my POV, her eyes, ice green crystals suddenly clear   like, I got myself a shot of hyper realism, free of charge, wham ! Those eyes, all a dazzle, as they are... Ah, gone now, the sight   the colour.   And herself as well, walking on. Think I fluffed it, but maybe ask again later in a few days, yeah, chance it...

Out! Screaming down the roadways on my trusty machine flexed up to the nines on company vision, now I'm winging it, singing it wild, all my cameras open wide to receive the world, riding on no-stop, through the ever-growing forests   of radio masts, where the world is broadcast daily, nightly, constantly, reality updated, me feeding it, and feeding off it, merging with it, imagine: me, clear of all fissures, blips, crackles, smears. And one day, I swear... No more little pixel squares, no more low rez shit, and better implants as well, replace these crappy lenses, had them since when, sixteen years old? Hell. Really? Begone, dull vision! I'll be the number one King of the All-Seeing Eye, you wait!!! Oh glory, glory be...

Later. Back home. Tommy looking at me   like he always does, all knowing, like, wink, wink. I've always suspected he has secret pixels, a little stash of his own, he never lets on, I hate that, but when he looks at me, it's like he knows me, he sees right through me, using some elaborate vision, sure of it

> REMEMBER: YOU ARE WHAT YOU SEE. YOU ARE WHAT YOU SEE

Tommy's job: selling his image to the texture companies. You spot him now and then, just popping up in modelled pixelworld scapes, watermarked, a standing figure, or striding through a forecourt or a marina, handsome devil, one hand pointing to the future, or at a boat, or whatever, proud, confident, oh sure, yeah, but like to punch him out one time, like to...

What the hell am I? What do I look like? Mirror: I can only see what I can see, a low-to-mid rez pixelhead, filtered by my lenses. But wonder: what do I look like really?

Out. Slow walk. A drink, need to... feel it, my eyes ache, the world, the city, the full moon, road signs, people all blurred, all the little cubes of life entangled, mashed together, cracking up, static interference, the curse of my rez level, and cheapo eye-tech. Look now: a pair of ever-circling dancing floating camera sprites homing in on me, their tiny little sparkling lenses wanting to capture my image, stream me. Ever growing numbers of them, getting everywhere these days, following, following... they call it the future of world-view... some of the bikecam companies have already gone bust... fuck, what would I do then, if..?

> DO YOU NEED MORE PIXELS? YES, YOU NEED MORE PIXELS! WE ALL NEED MORE PIXELS. TOP UP RIGHT NOW AT OUR NEAREST OUTLET

Need more pixels yes need more pixels, now more pixels...

Urge to buy instilled. Pop-ups get you like that sometimes, but what can

you do? Check into the corner kiosk, get myself a squirt of Low, keep it stable. Christ, a week till payday, I'll be down to the dregs before then, living on four or six pixels a day like some kind of crumble clown. But it feels like I'm running low already, what's wrong with me? Too many glitches. Fuck, close my eyes, move in darkness, yes, rest here, peaceful for a while, but even the dark is breaking up: little black cubes fragmenting and sliding away at the edge of greyness, as though the night is crumbling, crumbling...

Can't face the pub after all, too many people, to many viewpoints, all on me, and my image slightly different in each one, according to their pixel levels, and various enhancements: the noise, chaos of vision. On the bike today, those moments of blackout? Maybe not to do with the company's POV at all, but maybe to do with me? But what? What have I done wrong? Vision-sick? God, hope not, really

Moon nauseous yellow glow, ragged at the edge... street lamp blinding me, too much fuzziness, people all gaudy misshapes, girls in their eye-dazzling dresses, the guys ablaze with hatred, staggering drunk, looking at me, their faces shivery, breaking up

We're all caught in the present tense, how it is, this moment this one, now and now, this moment, and this one now and now now and now now now now now now there's no escaping it now and now... holy Christ, need to get away, streets too c rowded, too much info for my pix el level, can't... just ... just t can't fi lter it pro perly...

Alleyway yes dark here, better now, rest, breathe, Aiden. Aiden, Aiden you will get through this... A sprite follows, lens all aglow, watching me... LEAVE ME ALONE! Need to, need to grab it from the air, can't, no, try again, no, just out of reach... one squeeze would crack it open, images spilling out imagine, yes, all over my hands, just need to... grab, no, shit... Turn, run, keep moving, further, twisting alleyways... no lights...

blink

Wait, a **demo** will do it. Got some in my pocket, trusty supply. Pocket. Yes, crack it open and squeeze it in, good, at the temples, oh my little cheapest ever implants... now let's go crazy on **vision**, yes...

NOW!

Ah, sweet world of light and colour, so clear. The body. So clear, so present, filtered so. Yes, he's gone from this world. Finished. Brutal wounds, frenzy, no helping him. And there, at his fingertips, as though he's reaching out to touch, to retrieve, to keep hold of. What is that, a little black box [***] Damn it. Darkness now, sudden, a few seconds only, as always after a **demo**, dark, before the usual low rez kicks back in.

The camera-sprite still **floats** here, still watching me... I'm on **record**, I've been seen, witnessed...

Noise. Sirens, the cops, and my hands so red, so bloodied... Will have to... will have to run...

Home now. Safe. Hope so. But shaking still. Already used up yet another **demo** when I got in, first thing, just for the **buzz**, the surge of overload glow, needed it, like a whiskey **shot** to the eyes.

Alone. Tommy out. Good...

> OVERLOAD GLOW! OVERLOAD GLOW! OVERLOAD GLOW! NOTHING IMPROVES THE WORLD LIKE OVERLOAD GLOW! ORDER NOW...

That's the one. Automatic vizzipops for another hour, probably, as punishment for using the **demo**. Way it goes, life.

Wait, dead-end, locked steel door... back of a club, something
Trapped, no escape
You are what you see, remember... in the moments as they pass
Now, and now and now now now

nownownow now nownownownownow
the sprite sees me

stumble, fall
what...
vision blurring
to black

[***]

Nownow now now wake.... what?
Cold, on the ground, curled up, how?

How long? how long was I out for? What is that red colour, smudge of... blood yes blood here on my hands? What is that? Can't see properly, look look now...

A body, who? Unmoving cold, cold, so cold to the touch, can't see, blur, a boy, a man is it? Yes Oh God cold, dead my hands, the blood, how did this happen?

OK be calm, stay calm, just just, just just get it together. Look. Breathe. Examine. Get your fucking pixels together, kid! Stare. At the body. Concentrate!

OK. A man. Unknown, his face. And bloody, just like my... hands. All unknown, dressed in grey, a suit. How did he die? Knife, gun? But never heard anything... no, didn't. Don't know...

Bike. God, so good. Glory. The road. The road is liquid speed and here I zoom so sweet riding all the way down towards the vanishing point as it moves ahead of me just those few feet ahead like I can catch up with it one day soon if I just keep riding like this just keep moving and glowing yes this is the real overload the most perfect world ever and I am in it yes I am part of it with no vizzipops none just myself close to the centre gathering streaming skimming the tarmac and swerving so easy around the speeding cars no one can catch me no one can stop me, because now at last I see, yes fuck I feel the world in every pore, and there, a figure in my sight, not so clear, blurry, no, please, don't crumble away, not yet, let me stay here in this world, this version of the world, but strange, the figure moves, her form before me as I ride, a woman, it seems like, her face featureless, tightly covered in blue cloth, strange, never leaving me, who, who, who is she? [***]] Oh, awake, where... home.

But can't remember getting here.
Back to normal. Low Rez. Shitty squaresville. Old crumble zone.

The time, look at it. Bloody hell, I missed work today, did I? Just riding the city's streets for my own pleasure, hours on end. Wonder what my on-bike cameras captured; would love to access that. Need a code. Yes, but worth it, missing work,   just for the joy of the ride and the world as I travelled through it. Definitely. Or dreaming, was I? What? Fuck. Just maybe?

But no popjobs yet. None of the usual early morning flow of ads and feeds. Why is that?

The box. Still here. Wonder what it is, maybe   some kind of development, the future of improved sensual input. One more time, maybe?   No. Resist, resist...

Round at Bella's pad. Talking in dim light, shadows, her   face

The little box. On my bed. Yes, mine now. Stolen. Black metal, no shine, silver filligree patterns. Warm to the touch.   Stolen. Oh God, why? Not like me, not at all. What is it, I wonder? Nothing on the news feed yet, about the dead body. Wonder who?

Why did he die? Frenzied attack. Maybe just a robbery gone wrong? But why not take the box? So then it's not worth anything? Wonder? If I... that is, if I open it... no, can't do it, won't budge, sealed, no opening? What? My fingers find a little ridge, and push... hissing sound... *hssssssst* Strange. Feel... No. Nothing. Sleep now, sleep...

YOU ARE WHAT YOU SEE

Wait. But the sprites that follow, follow? Think! What if, I was... captured there, on record, in the alley next to the body. Rumours: that sprites see reality, the real deal, the world as it is, the never seen, never felt, never heard, the world behind the veil of pixels... wonder what I, what I look like, there.... Zero Rez, they call it, NO REZ. The unmediated world, cold analog, urgh, scary, makes me, makes me shiver... feel sick. The stories they tell of what remains, naked of pixels: a place of dirt, decay, ruin, weeds, rust, trash, dust, silence, the void, rats, infestation, disease, the Desert of the Real...

Up. Good sleep finally, that dream, what what was it, so clear, like I could see every detail of life. **No blur, no smears,** no crumble at the edges. **Strange.** Dreaming: my face covered all over in blue cloth, why? I feel...

What am I **seeing now** the room... my **room, so clear.** So vivid, dazzling, so damn vivid, **alive to my eyes, my senses, my hands touching at the tabletop, where every grain can be felt, every detail present in the moment,** filtered to high heaven, all the way. Perfected, as I am... as I **gather the room to myself via the senses: so clear, so sweet, so goddamn fucking sweet, everything, mine, my world, mine...**

rumours at all, but all grey goo on the screen, with just this single little dot of **high rez** floating around; Bella explains it: some kind of privacy law, sprites only allowed to focus on one **thing** after another, whatever's deemed important: **me, there,** for instance, **down the alleyway,** following me... **the dead-end**... doorway, there, the **body of** the **man... dead,** there, **myself**... looking down at **him... swaying,** feel it, remember...

Blackout. As myself, as I did then, on that night, so the screen does now. Crash. What? What now? Where? Bella punches keys, works the controls, curses. Nothing. Dead screen. Wiped clean. Zero reveal. Until... until the world clicks back into place, into view and now I'm caught once more in sprite mode, sirens in the night sky calling out, calling, and me, that young man there, that scared young man with the blood on his hands, me, myself, running running...

Bella warns me: somebody's protecting the victim. Erasure in place. Tells me: Aiden, dearest, be careful.

Home again. Straight to the box, can't resist. Just can't. Yes. Have to. Urge. Memories burn, need to feel that sense of life again, up close, that heavenly vision fix, streaming me with colours and sound and light. Press. *Hsssssssst.* Yes, slight perfume. Vapour of some **kind, maybe? Yes. Wonder...**

Walking this time. Slow, steady. Taking in the city in all its beauty, magnified, made glorious, everywhere I look crammed to the very limits with pixels, so many of them, thousands upon thousands, squeezed together, so perfectly arranged in the mosaic that I can see no joins, no edges, only the smooth surface of life, but with the colours turned up, the sharpness increased, the contrast set at its highest ratio, and everything so scorchingly lovely to look at, so shimmery, so vibrant, the people especially, their faces, their bodies, I can hardly

scattermasked, against, as she says, the intruding beams of the corporate targeting engines, invisible they are, nanosprites, or so she claims, like dust in the air, getting in through the cracks in the walls, the ceiling, recording everything, all over...

Crazy for sure. But maybe...

She gives me a **dose of pixel power, a one minute shot, something she's concocted herself from hacked supplies... nice,** but it's nothing like the **effects** of the **hyperbox,** as I'm calling it. But I can't tell her about that. No, not yet. **Secret.** But why? Just for me. Really? OK. Is that wise? Stay dumb. Just ask about sprite-cams: the need to access footage, such and such a time, location, when I was alleyway bound, that blackout moment, the dead man on the cold ground, need to need to know what happened...

Bella's legit business is selling images, a whole library of things she's collected over the years: flowers, fields, sunsets, rockets taking off, semi naked dancers, goals being scored, cheering or rioting crowds, whatever you need to complete your reality. Little extras, accessories to life. Some of them have watermarks in them, because she's stolen the pictures, but who cares, really?

Some of the best things I've ever seen, ever... have been watermarked. Like that time I with Katie, when I... shit, concentrate...

Always a pleasure watching Bella break a code wide open, or a little sliver of a way in, her fingers on the console, twitching, game-play really, no different... back to DOS, her favoured mode, retrotech. The console brightening under her touch, the screen alive with image, and there, there I am... look now...

That night. The street. As the sprites see me, but it's weird, not like the

Tommy's back, I hear. The door banging. Why won't he come in, oh... strange, not like him, no call out, no shout to me, no stories of his conquests, of the ever marvellous journeys his image has gone on today in Texture Land... Oh... not him, what? Who?

Two of them. Strangers. Men.   Dark. Uh. Lights out. What? What do they want? I can't... I can't see them. Fuck. Have to, I have to get out of here... now...

Noises, footsteps, a grunt. My body folding up as the first blow hits. Stomach. Crack. On the head, fuck, something heavy, where... I can't, have to move, have to crawl...

They're going for my implants... tearing at them...

Another blow. Pixels jumping in my eyes, breaking apart, the room crumbles and I fall, with no way to know where to go, no world, no room, only patterns as the pixels drain away, crazy dancing as the two men circle around me, have to fight back, but they're jacked up on some kind of vision high, the both of them, I can sense that: they know everything about me, where to strike, how to lead me on, how to defend themselves, their POVs blaze with power, imagine...

Have to... crack! **Demo**. Use it. Now. **Sizzle and flare, sudden, and there! The first man, there! Strike out and he reels back** [***] fuck, darkness, where now, where, crack, one more. **Demo**, fumbling for... now **now now there he is, the second man, charge for him, push with him full strength all I have left, into the wall the two of us, crack!** [***] dark, where, dark, both of them coming in, blows all around, I'm down, fumble, crackle, **demo** where? **There, so clear, these last few seconds of visual bliss as the blows rain down, and here's me, thinking, thinking... if only I had my little hyperbox with me, beat them then** [***] yes, beat them then, easily...

look at them for fear of melting my eyeballs with such radiant beauty. And this is life as it should be lived, at the highest level of POV, here in this paradise... [***] Like a jump cut, one time to another, and what's been lost in between, I don't know, I do not care, the neon signs flash and glow with fiery reds and shining golds and blues the colour of music as it drifts free of the sign, above me and around me now, the words singing out their meaning plain, but only I can hear them, only I have this much data in my sight [***] I see the sprites as they follow me dancing floating along for what they are: the never-sleeping eyes of the world, watching, the one million eyes of the city, watching watching watching targeting... and what happens when all the eyes close at once, yes what then? [***] Among the crowd only one person still seems unclear, the blue figure again, moving in and out of vision as though she exists between the pixels, as though there might be another layer of resolution beyond this one, but how can there be, how can the world be more prefect than this? And yet there she stands, watching me, and now she moves, the woman, her face without features, covered in blue, her whole body also, blue, blue cloth, head to foot, as she turns as though to look at me, but her eyes hidden, and then she moves on and I follow her, try to, yes...

Broken now. **Broken**. I feel. Broken. Without the high rez. Lost. Bereft. Wandering. The effect lasts for about an hour, on average. But I can't stop using it. Can't stop. Will it run out, ever? **Panic**. Will the hyperbox run out of vapour, whatever it is. It must do, eventually. And then, and then what? How will I face the world ever again, like this, in this low rez gutter?

Once or twice: little **flashbacks**,   but then   nothing, so   cruel...

What are we walking toward, quite willingly, I wonder? We are walking into the eye of the camera, a gleeful smile on our faces, our eyes satiated with streamed reality, ever-changing, ever, ever-changing, where does it lead, wonder...

Gone. Alone. Stir. Awake. Head aching, body, scarred, bloody. Bruises. Painful to move. Where? Can't seem to find my.... uh   bearings

Alone now, sure of it, don't breathe just listen. Listen!   No one. Gone now, they've gone, and taken what they came for, the box, the vapour, the Resolution of the Gods, stolen from me, as I stole it from the mugging victim, whoever he was, and the two men knew, they knew precisely what they wanted, why they came here...

Something's wrong, my eyes, crumble of sight, vision, all the sense, I'm losing focus, the room...

The rooms, all of them, disintegrating as I walk through them, I'm losing...

I'm losing pixels, drifting, crackling, the edges of my POV drifting apart

Implants, damaged   must get help... police or get Tommy, Katie   Bella
yes   anybody

Can't see, only six colours now   in my vision,   five,   four, sinking

No   don't move, ride it, ride it out! Maybe it's temporary, has to be...

Down to two colours now, a few cubes left to me,   squares, so low, ragged,   where am I,
Where   am I heading... wonder...

blink
colours flashing, disappearing
one pixel
as though falling, falling asleep, but

but different now, sinking

---

flicker
blink , blink blink...

click
zero

zero rez
blink

dark, darkness in the eyes
blink
blink

only
darkness
only...

[***]

Where?
where now
blink
stir
stir awake
the world
outside

moving, moving on
crawling, stumbling, walking
I am the dirt on the surface of objects
the rip in the cloth
grease on the lens
yes, feel it now
I am the grain in the wood

the warp in the plastic
the grit in the engine
the dirt, the grease, the smears
the damage, the grain, the warp, the friction
all magnified, all glorious, yes, at last
I am the touch of flesh on flesh
of tongue and teeth on food
words on lips, tears to the eyes, vibrations
I am the zero world, shorn of pixels
down to the skin and bone and breath, pure
the mist, the dirty polluted rain so fresh on the face, uplifted
the rust that eats at the cars that sit abandoned at the roadside
the lovely rust, that parasite of metals
the streets blown by litter and leaves
the unpainted walls, the rotten fruit
the cats and dogs snuffling at the gutter
and myself seeing as the dogs see
hearing as they do, roused by the same scents
following trails through the desolate almost empty streets
and a few others here as well, now and then, like myself
people who have moved away from the camera's ever-watchful eye
and Colleen herself, as lovely today
as she was when she first stepped out from in-between the pixels
to wave at me, to call to me
dressed in blue as she is, so strange, her face still covered, still unseen, strange
and she leads me on towards the edge of the city
to where the many colours of the streets, the buildings, all start to fade
all into blue, the same exact shade as she wears on her body
the shops, the road signs, all covered in blue cloth, strange
and other people, more and more of them, all wearing the same blue outfits
and myself also, I realise now, as we reach the city's limit
dressed in the same blue
and I see now that for all these years I have forgotten

as we all have, the deal we made:
that our city, our lives, our loves and hates, our flesh, our faces
are but projections on this endless blue screen
that stretches around us, covering us

and now we move on
away from the projectors' reach, far away
into the areas beyond the city, where the endless blue fields
touch the endless blue skies
with no visible horizon separating them
only the blue world, endless, endless...
until the blue starts to fray a little
and at last we kiss, Colleen and I
our two faces covered in cloth
our covered mouths, now touching
where our fingers tear the cloth away
and now our eyes are seen, uncovered
the blue cloth on our faces in shreds
and now Colleen reaches out to the distant sky
and her hand touches the sky, a few feet away
the blue cloth sky, and she takes a penknife
clicks out the blade, the tiny shining blade
and slices into the blue
and together, at last, at last, we climb through
and now, at long last, yes, finally

we are what we see

Jeff Noon was born in Manchester in 1957. His novels include *Vurt* (Arthur C. Clarke Award), *Pollen*, *Automated Alice*, *Nymphomation*, *Needle in the Groove*, *Cobralingus*, *Falling Out of Cars*, *Channel SK1N*, and a collection of stories called *Pixel Juice*. He also writes microfiction via @ jeffnoon on Twitter, and on Facebook. More information can be found at jeffnoon.weebly.com. This is his first appearance in *Interzone*.

C.A. HAWKSMOOR MURDER ON THE
LAPLACIAN EXPRESS

ILLUSTRATED BY WARWICK FRASER-COOMBE

It's all right," Shai Laren said as Anselm swung down into the driver's cabin of the *Laplacian Express*. "I'm almost sure I know how to fly this thing."

Anselm stepped through the haze of bitter smoke pouring from the split control panel, almost stumbling over something obscured underneath it. "Where's the driver?"

Shai didn't look up from what was left of the controls, but the iridophores in her skin rippled blue and green with irritation. "I believe you have just found him."

"Ah." Anselm leaned out into the snarl of Martian wind. "What about landing? Can you do landing?"

Shai Laren flipped one of the switches and the thrum of the interstellar engine dropped by a full tone. "Maybe," she said. "Give me time."

Anselm rested back against the bulkhead and crossed his arms. "So long as you can do it before we plough into the side of that ravine, take all you time you need."

"Ravine?" Her eyes flashed purple then drained back to silver-blue.

Pointless trying to get the overhead display to boot up. She stepped into the open door and leaned out as he had done. The wind was a billion grains of hard red sand, superheated by the bright white thrusters underneath the train. It was like putting her head into a blast furnace. Shai turned away. Her headtresses washed over her face as she looked back down the silver ribbon of the express train glinting blue and violet in the sunset.

She held her breath and turned back into the wind. It cracked against her ear drums and then everything went as quiet as cotton wool. Beyond the horizon, the verdant green of the agrisphere was rising in front of the night's first stars. She watched it getting swallowed by the half a mile high wall of jagged red cliff-face emerging from the rusty shadows of the desert.

Shai ducked back inside and pulled the headtresses out of her face. "Yes," she said. "I can see the problem. That isn't good."

Her eyes met Anselm's through the smoke. He was still leaning calmly against the bulkhead, the veil torn back from his face so that she could see the golden weave of filigree over his skin. She looked away quickly, but her skin flushed with thick purple stripes before she could stop herself.

"You don't look much better, I assure you," Anselm said crisply. "And no, it isn't good. I quite agree. Perhaps you would like to try and stop this thing before it stops itself and kills us all?"

Shai flipped another switch and slammed the flat of her hand against a dead section of the console. It flickered for a moment, and came to life. "If you'll stop bothering me for just one moment, doula," she said, "then I will see what I can do."

....

The night before, the two of them had stood in the middle of the largest interplanetary station on the surface of Jupiter, waiting for the *Laplacian Express* to pull up to the platform. The station was an ornate two mile dome of brass and polished glass rising out of the Jovian jungle and lit by a million hovering lanterns. Filled up with spices, animals, traders, and passengers from all over the Solar System. But to the ancient machine that nestled at the back of Shai Laren's neck and wove its filigree-light exoskeleton over her body, she was still standing in the centre of a rainforest.

It had been clear-cut more than a century ago now, but the jungle rushed in to fill the darkness behind her closed eyelids so quickly that she was almost floating in it. A cold grey sky drifted above the canopy. Leaves heavy and slapping wet against her skin. She was like polished terracotta. Lean and strong and fierce. A Jovian huntress. And she was running. Running through ruins engulfed in twisted roots and vines. Something out there among the trees. She didn't know if she was hunting it, or it was hunting her.

"Shai, pay attention."

Anselm's voice snapped her back into herself. Suddenly there was too much light and too much noise. The night was so thick outside that the glass dome was polished black. Shai almost felt the pneuma machina curling against the base of her skull, aching after that lost ruin in the jungle. She wiped at the tears that stood in her eyes, thankful for the white linen wrappings that covered the scrollwork of her exoskeleton, but also hid the deep wave of blue longing that surged up through the chromatic cells in her skin.

She glanced across at Anselm awkwardly. "Yes, doula."

He linked his hands behind his back and stared out into the crowd. "You should enter resonance when you choose," he said. "Not whenever the pneuma machina whims it."

Shai looked down at her feet. "Yes, doula."

Anselm nodded. "Good. Now then, I think our charge is here."

Shai raised her head and rolled onto the balls of her feet to get a better view. The air was warm as bathwater, full of the smell of incense and cooking food. She focused her mind and pushed down that feeling of floating in the jungle. The prickle of strange eyes prising into her from somewhere amongst the trees. The bustle of black body armour around Chief Executive Lascelles stood out almost as much as Shai and Anselm did in the veils and simple linen wrappings of the Syzygian Church. The guards formed a wall around Lascelles that even light could barely penetrate.

Anselm put his hand onto the wrappings of Shai's shoulder. "Come on."

They wove through the crowd easily, their pneuma machina drinking in the data of their senses and performing a thousand tiny calculations on the location and velocity of every other moving creature in their paths. The data surged down the tracery of Shai's exoskeleton like blood. All she had to do was allow her muscles to relax and respond to the touch of the machine. It was not yet as intuitive to her as it was to Anselm. After a few feet she slipped in silently behind him to let him feel out the path.

"Tell me about her?" she said. It probably wasn't proper protocol, but the keepers in the Cathedral on Saturn had warned her that Anselm was considered unconventional even for a human. Perhaps he would respond well to some initiative.

He glanced back over his shoulder, everything but the deep green of his eyes covered by his veil. "Chief Executive Lascelles is on the board of the Lilienthal Mining Company." Speaking to her did not seem to interfere with his navigating the crowd. Most people saw the wrappings of the Syzygian Church and simply got out of his way, making it easy for his pneuma machina to guide him smoothly around the rest. "In addition to their conventional mining activities, Lilienthal also runs a number of correctional vessels."

"You mean prison ships?"

Anselm nodded uncomfortably. "The ships function as mobile refineries. They collect the ore from the surface mines in the various asteroid fields and deliver blocks of finished metal and machine parts to the drop-off points on Earth, Mars, or wherever else— Excuse me, terribly sorry."

Anselm stepped around the lumbering body of a Cronian. It turned its head to watch them go. How unusual it felt to see one of them outside of the Cathedral. Shai's pneuma machina detected the patterns of the Cronian's consciousness reverberating against her own and responded with the equivalent of a psychic handshake before she even knew what she was doing. The Cronian nodded slowly and lumbered off into the crowd.

"Six months ago," Anselm was saying. "The prisoners rioted on board one of Lilienthal's correctional vessels, the *Queen of Heaven*. Since then, there have been four assassination attempts against members of the company's board. Three of them successful."

Shai frowned. "You think the prisoners on board the Queen of Heaven have found some way to kill those responsible for the prison ship," she said. "As revenge?"

Anselm nodded. "The Eye would like us to ensure that Executive Lascelles' trip to the trade conference on Mars is blissfully uneventful."

Before Shai had the chance to reply, they came up against the living wall of Executive Lascelles' security team. Their visors were all down so that they were indistinguishable from one another, but it was the one in the centre that spoke.

"Out of the way, please."

"Ah!" Anselm said affably. "Yes! Warden Alladice, is it? Executive Lascelles mentioned you were thorough. Very good. She is, however, expecting us."

The Warden shook his head slowly, his visor reflecting the light of the thousand tiny coloured lanterns hovering above. "I believe I would know about it if we were expecting—"

"And if you listened to me for even one moment," a voice came from within the crush of bulletproofed body armour, "then you would do."

The security team hesitated for a moment and then parted around an ageing human woman in an angular and ugly suit that probably cost more money than Shai Laren would see in her whole lifetime. Shai's eyes skipped to the Selenite in a simple black dress at her side. Selenites were still a rare sight beyond Earth's wasting atmosphere and Her few remaining Lunar colonies. Shai had not seen another member of her species since she was a little girl. The Selenite's skin scrolled red-gold and deep pink in a cautious greeting, and for the first time since her Anointment, Shai felt stifled in her wrappings.

"Anselm," Executive Lascelles was saying, taking his hands in her own and clasping them together. "I would recognise that voice anywhere. How are you? It's been too long."

"Far too long, Chief Executive," Anselm agreed, bringing her fingers to his veil as though he meant to kiss them.

Lascelles smiled, flattered. "It's Marjory, Anselm, and I am so glad the Church could spare you."

Anselm dipped his head in a small bow. "It was my pleasure."

"And you have a new initiate with you too, I see."

It took Shai Laren a moment to realise that they were talking about her. A jolt of sudden embarrassment shot through her body, the thick purple stripes reaching all the way into the gap in her veil. When she looked up, Lascelles was still staring.

"And Selenite too, is she? My my. How very exotic. I wasn't aware the Empire allowed them to join the Syzygian Church."

Anselm inclined his head a little. "Not all of her people belong to the Empire. Shai Laren was born in a dancing hall back on Earth. When the company folded, the Church offered her sanctuary."

Lascelles nodded. "Very charitable of you," she said. "Yes. Very charitable. Well then, girl, let's see you. Take off those wrappings and let me have a proper look."

Shai Laren's eyes crept to Anselm, but he only shifted his weight awkwardly and looked away. She started with the veil, unfastening it on one side and then the other before unwinding the longer wrappings about her head. She ran her fingers through her headtresses, which mottled yellow-brown when the cool air touched them before returning to the almost-white of moonstone.

Executive Lascelles took Shai's chin between her thumb and forefinger and studied her carefully. "I prefer you like that," she pronounced. "Leave them off."

She offered Anselm her arm and they turned away before Shai had the chance to protest. The *Laplacian Express* was rolled into the station almost silently. Half a mile of mirror-polished steel and glass. Endless cabins of sparking crystal and thick purple velvet behind its windows. Warden Alladice yelled at the security team to bring the Executive's bags and clear the way to the cabin, while Shai fell in beside the other Selenite.

"I'm Shai," she said.

The other woman's skin mottled caution, although Shai noticed an unfamiliar green colouring along the exposed lengths of her arms. The meaning of the pattern was beyond her, but it made her feel safer.

"Serethi," she said. "Although it pleases the Executive to call me Selene."

Shai flushed with irritation and she looked up at Lascelles.

"Do the two of you have plans for dinner?" she was asking. "You must join me. No really, I insist."

Serethi took a blank disk of wet clay from the small bag at her hip and incised a number of small marks into it with the edge of her fingernail. She did it swiftly. Automatically. Without taking her eyes from the train. Shai folded it up into the sleeve of her wrappings just as quickly. Their eyes met for a moment. Then Lascelles called for Serethi, the doors of the *Laplacian Express* whispered open, and all of them were swallowed by the crush of bodies, light, and sound.

■■ I've seen those before," Anselm remarked, carefully re-pinning his veil. Shai Laren averted her eyes. "The slave dancers in many of the theatres on Earth exchange them as trinkets."

Shai Laren turned the clay coin between her thumb and forefinger, letting it dry underneath the desk lamp. "They're more than that. We – the Selenites, I mean – they use them to share information amongst themselves."

She was almost certain that she shouldn't be telling him, but she gave up any loyalty to the rest of her species when she joined the Syzygian Church. The keepers were very specific.

Anselm glanced away from the small mirror wedged into a corner of their cabin, his fingers still thoughtlessly brushing at the dirt on his sleeve. "And what information does that one have for us?"

Shai frowned, trying to work out which way up it was meant to go. "It's…not easy for me to tell," she said. "I was never taught much about Selenite culture before the Church took me, and I'm sure I've forgotten most of what I knew when I was small."

It wasn't a complete lie, but even Shai could make out the eyes and open mouth incised into the centre. The lines pointing outwards from it that meant danger. She turned it over and studied the reverse. The marks there were obviously intended to be a number, although she couldn't tell which one. The curved line a representation of the moon. Or the Selenites. Or perhaps Serethi herself.

Anselm turned his attention back on his reflection. "You should get ready for dinner," he said, and when she did not respond: "Is something the matter, Shai?"

"I… No, doula. It's only…this ship is very strange and it moves more than I am used to. I feel a little unwell, that's all."

"That's hardly unusual," he said lightly. "It is after all very different to any vessel that you have been on board before." He frowned for a moment, drew a breath, and stepped back from the mirror. "Perhaps you should stay here and rest. I'm sure the nausea will wear off once we are above the atmosphere."

Shai remembered the way that he had kissed Executive Lascelles' hands on the station. The way that Lascelles had looked at him. She dipped her head in agreement.

"Thank you, doula," she said. "I'm certain that you're right."

....

Finding some space to move around on board the *Laplacian Express* was harder than it seemed. It took Shai almost a full hour to happen upon a mostly empty baggage car towards the back of the train. The silver bulkheads were exposed, the sound of the thrusters raw through the scuffed steel, and the coldness of space seeped into every nook.

It didn't matter. At least she was alone.

Shai stood still in the centre of the carriage. Eyes closed. Just listening to the resonance of the thrusters. The resonance of the blood in her own veins. Of the machine coiled about her hindbrain. The pneuma machina was reluctant tonight, as though it was watching from a distance to see what she would do. But then Anselm was insistent that those were the moments when she most needed to practise.

She relaxed every muscle in her body one after another. Breathing and listening and waiting. And when the machine quietened into compliance, she danced. The more she moved her body, the more she became aware of its position in space and time. Of every minor adjustment in the muscles running from her feet, through her core, to her arms and her neck. She didn't force the pneuma machina to guide her. Just allowed her body to move and waited for it to join in. For flesh and circuitry to melt into one another, twisting her body around impossibly quickly and smoothly, the filigree of her exoskeleton supporting her until she could push her weight right up onto the very tips of her toes…

"You move so beautifully."

The voice brought Shai back into herself with a jolt. Everything came apart in a clattering chaos that sent the blankness of her mind spiralling out into a thousand different thoughts. She almost lost her footing and reached out to steady herself on the bulkhead.

Serethi stood in the doorway, her skin cells patterning with a mixture of apology and amusement. "There are dancers in the slave pools on Earth who spend their whole lives learning to move their bodies and never manage to be so fluid." She walked forwards slowly, stretching out a finger towards the tracery of brass-gold metal woven over Shai Laren's skin. "Is it something to do with this? I heard someone say that you are fused to a machine."

Shai Laren pulled a face. "We call it Anointment," she said. "The pneuma machina aren't like the modern cybernetic implants that the Gradivusi make on Mars. They are very old and powerful. They get to choose who they want to be joined with. I…like to dance. The keepers encouraged me to keep doing it when I was brought to the Cathedral. After you've been Anointed, you have to figure out how to let the machine co-operate with you. How to allow it to move for you, because they can work so much quicker and more precisely than our brains can. Perform a billion calculations about our weight and speed in every second. Learning how to surrender to the machine, but also to guide it to doing what you want it to do…they call it going into resonance."

Serethi inclined her head a little and traced a curl of golden metal from Shai's cheek to her jawline. "That's what you were doing then," she said. And, when Shai nodded: "Can it feel me touching it?"

Shai laughed. "It's not like that," she said. "It isn't separate from me anymore. Me, the machine, the memories it has of all of the people that it was joined to before me…we're all the same now."

Serethi drew her hand away and crossed her arms loosely, her skin showing uncertainty. Apprehension. "Executive Lascelles says that you are in some kind of church."

"The keepers call it a Church, and I guess the Cathedral on Saturn looks like one. Only we don't worship any gods."

"So…what do you worship?"

Shai struggled for a moment. "Just…the universe, I suppose. The patterns of it."

"Like physics?"

Shai shrugged. "Sure, that's part of it." She felt the pneuma machina thrum against her thoughts. "I couldn't read the coin well, but I thought you might come to find me. Ever since I met you, you've seemed…scared."

Shai sat down cross-legged on the floor and leant her back against the bulkhead. For as long as she could remember, she'd felt like a lost child wandering an impossibly huge universe. It was strange to be the one who wasn't afraid. She motioned for Serethi to sit beside her. "Do you want to tell me what you're scared of?"

Serethi scoffed and looked at her hands. "What aren't I scared of?" she said. "One wrong word to the Chief Executive and I'm back in the slave pools on Earth. But that's…that's not why I'm here. I heard Major Alladice talking. About the *Queen of Heaven*. About how we're going to

Mars so that Executive Lascelles can attend the trade conference."

Shai nodded and waited for her to finish. Serethi hesitated for a long time. The tone of the thrusters grew deeper and fuller as the *Laplacian Express* finally slid free of the last of Jupiter's gravity.

"The say the Syzygian Church are good people," Serethi said at last. "That you're not like everybody else. If that's true, then you and your master should stop her before she gets to that conference."

Shai Laren frowned. "Why?"

Serethi's skin surged red-orange. "Because a lot of people are going to die if you don't," she snapped. She took a couple of breaths to let the colour drain away. "The Executive has me take all of her letters and messages down. The prisoners on board that ship, the *Queen of Heaven*, they are entirely dependant on everybody planet-side to help. Their ships can't enter the atmosphere. There are some places out in the colonies… docks that are controlled by the big unions that Lascelles has spent the last few years trying to wipe out…they're giving the *Queen of Heaven* support. Resupplying her with food and oxygen. She's going to the conference to convince the companies that own those places to lock their people out until the *Queen of Heaven* surrenders. Only… Only I'm not sure that she *wants* them to surrender. She wants them to suffocate. To use the whole thing to turn people against the last few unions still clinging on out there. Make it look like their fault somehow. I don't…I don't understand the details."

Shai shifted her weight uncomfortably. "That's terrible."

"She believes that if she doesn't crush the *Queen of Heaven* and the unions that are supporting her, then dissent could spread to the other prison ships. That they could lose a fortune. All any of them care about is their share price. And why wouldn't they? It's not like they know what it's like to be stuck somewhere. To be utterly dependant on someone else to keep you alive…"

Shai Laren got to her feet. "Then we have to make them understand," she said. "Come along. My doula is a good man, even if he is human. He'll listen to me, I know it."

"Absolutely not."

Anselm strode through the narrow corridors between the sleeping compartments, heading for First Class. Shai Laren had to break into a trot to keep up.

"But doula, Serethi said—"

"It doesn't matter," he cut her off. "The Eye sent us here to fulfil an order. Not to play politics. It is not our place, Shai."

"Not even when hundreds of people could die?"

"The men and women on that ship are all murderers, thieves, and terrorists," he said. "They had their chance to serve the punishment meted out by their societies, instead they chose open revolution. It is up to the planetary governments and companies to decide how to react, not you."

Shai reached out and grabbed the sleeve of his wrappings. "Then what are we even doing here? Why didn't those companies and the governments send their own people to watch over the Executive? Why would the Eye intervene in this matter and ask us to go? Unless…the Church was responding to your personal request."

"What in the stars are you talking about? Let go of me."

Shai released his sleeve and stepped back. "You obviously know the Executive," she said. "Is it fair that you should be involved in this, when you obviously have feelings for her?"

"You speak out of turn, Shai. Be careful that you don't come to regret it."

The threat stopped her cold. She thought about returning to the stone corridors of the Cathedral. Even of going back to the dance halls on Earth that they had plucked her from as a child. About what the Church would do if Anselm decided that she was too much trouble. Decided that she could not be taught. And then she thought about the *Queen of Heaven*, drifting helpless through the cold dark and slowly running out of air…

"Now," Anselm said. "I have to check the forward section before we land. Can I trust you to watch over the Executive while I am gone, or must I confine you to quarters until all of this is over?" He stopped beside a carved door where Warden Alladice was standing guard and turned around to face her.

Shai felt her skin mottle with rage. "I will do my duty, doula."

Anselm nodded. "Good. Now, if you will excuse me?" He didn't wait for an answer, but turned and walked into the dining car, leaving the door swinging behind. Shai Laren watched him disappear into the tinkling of crystal, the warm light fracturing through the chandelier, and the laughter of the guests. She took up her place on the other side of Lascelles' room and balled her hands up into fists. Warden Alladice glanced curiously across at her, but said nothing.

Difficult to tell how long she stood there before the light changed in the dining car and the blast shields rolled down over the windows. A chime sounded in the tiny speakers set into the moulded plaster ceiling and a sweet artificial voice washed over the faint hum of the engines.

"Attention all passengers. We shall shortly be descending into the atmosphere of Mars. Our expected arrival time at Oculus Station is four minutes past twelve bells, standard time. Please return to your seats and ensure that your restraint belts are correctly fastened until the blast shields are lifted. Thank you."

Shai Laren raised her head slightly to listen, nodded, and linked her hands behind her back.

Warden Alladice glanced sideways. "Perhaps we should do as it says."

Shai Laren frowned. "Anselm has charged me with keeping watch over the Executive," she said. "I am not about to shirk my duty."

"Very well then," he said. "I will do the same."

The train began to shudder with the stresses of re-entry. Warden Alladice reached out to steady himself on the door frame, but Shai only allowed the pneuma machina to find the point of perfect balance. She closed her eyes and for a moment she could almost feel the atmosphere of Mars rushing past. Tiny particles racing over her skin in trails of blue and gold. It took her some time to separate out the shouting in the dining car from the gentle roar of the re-entry.

A wave of nauseous apprehension rippled through her body a moment before an explosion of raygun fire turned the air to a prickle of lightning. The sound slammed against her body like the blow of an open hand. Someone started screaming. Moving on her toes to absorb some of the turbulence, Shai Laren slammed into the dining car. In all of the commotion it was difficult to tell the shooter from the bystanders. Her eardrums hazed with white noise as the pneuma machina sifted out the useful information, isolating one voice amongst a hundred.

"—these monsters won't stop until they have bled us dry. Every one of us! The *Queen of Heaven* is not our enemy! These people just want the same basic rights to life as you. As your own sons and daughters. It is barbaric to keep them sealed up there in the vacuum and the darkness, forcing them to work and threatening them with death if they do not comply.

"You think that you are ruled by your planetary governments? These companies own each and every one of you. And we aren't sentient creatures to these corporations. We're cattle!"

A man's body was lying prone on the floor. Shai could smell the sharpness of ionised particles. The sickening char of burning meat. She crouched down as she reached the body, but the crowd pushed her out of the way before she could feel for a pulse. Shai had no choice but to head for the man with the raygun. He was wearing a badge on the lapel of his tattered jacket – red and shaped like a star with an open hand within. She raised her voice over the screams.

"There's a storm on Venus that's raged for more than a thousand years," she said. "The Cythereans call it the Spectre Unchained."

He stopped speaking. His face knotted with confusion as he tried to fit the information into what was happening around him. It was one of the first things the keepers had taught her to avoid drawing her fanblade. Still her favourite when facing someone so pumped with adrenaline and cortisone that their whole perception of the world was narrowed to a pinpoint.

"I…" he began shakily, all the certainty gone out of him. "I don't…"

"Amongst some Gradivusi," she said, taking another step forwards, "it's considered grossly offensive to ask a direct question to anything but a close friend or family member."

She had his full attention now. He was Mercurial. One of the lower castes from the look of his six fingers. There had been a Mercurial in the Cathedral who could trace her ancestry three thousand years, and boasted two full sets of eight fingers and three thumbs. He stood out amongst the opulent interior of the *Laplacian Express*. His chalk white skin and hair almost a negative space.

"What…"

Shai held out her hand. "Give me the gun," she said.

The Mercurial hesitated for a moment, his eyes darting amongst the passengers who were still trying to climb over each other to escape. It looked like he might shoot her anyway, and Shai reached for the hilt of her fanblade. Then a hand emerged from the crowd behind the shooter, plucking the raygun out of his six fingers. The Mercurial started shouting, but moments later two of the train's robotic security team were wrestling him to the floor.

Anselm dropped the raygun into a half-finished tureen of soup and reached out to take her elbow, turning back towards the sleeping cabins. "Panic over," he said.

This time, Shai Laren could get close enough to the man lying on the fine carpets to be sure that he was dead. She sighed and stood with him for a moment until the security team came. Stupid, really. But it seemed like the least she could do. As they took him away, she looked back over her shoulder.

"How many of the assassination attempts did you say had succeeded so far, doula?"

Anselm frowned at her. "Four attempts. Three successful." And when she kept staring back at the Mercurial spitting and swearing into the pile of the carpet. "What is it, Shai?"

"Assuming that the other targets had a comparable level of security," she said. "This would appear to be a particularly inept assassination attempt."

Anselm shrugged. "Perhaps he is a particularly inept assassin," he said. "Perhaps he has nothing to do with the others. When we reach the Oculus station the Gradivusi will take him into custody. We can question him then."

Shai nodded and kept walking, but did not look convinced. When they reached Executive Lascelles' door they took up their places on either side.

Anselm looked around. "Where's Warden Alladice?"

Shai's chromatophores pulsed. "He was here before," she said. "Perhaps he saw what was going on and decided to check on the Executive? Anselm, wait—"

Anselm opened the door. The blast shields were slowly scrolling back from the windows, bathing everything in Martian twilight – an ever-changing collage of red-orange sand, purple sky, and burned umber shadows that made everything inside the cabin look like it was moving. Layered in rippling light. Warden Alladice was a curve of concentrated shadow bending over Executive Laselles' bed. Silver reflections from the orbital array spun themselves into the evening cloud and caught on the knife in his hand. Shai Laren reached for her fanblade, but Anselm had already drawn. His blade came open in an arch of brass-coloured metal that hung in the air as Warden Alladice spat with pain and the knife clattered to the floor in two shards of severed metal.

Anselm's fanblade folded back into itself and the Warden backed away from them both, pressing against the windows where the surface of Mars crested slowly into view behind. In the silence, Shai Laren could hear herself breathing over the pulse of the engines. Then the windows shattered outwards. For a moment, Alladice hung in the roaring gale that shredded his black cloak into rags. Then he reached out almost in slow motion and curled up onto the roof of the train.

Anselm rushed to the Executive's side and Shai Laren hesitated – her hand still resting on her fanblade.

"Go after him, Shai!" Anselm's voice cracked over the wind. "Or we'll lose him. Quickly!"

It took her a moment to realise what he was saying. After that, she didn't have time to be incredulous. Shai covered the small cabin in three fast steps and swung herself up into the wind. It roared through her headtresses and burned in her eyes, but the air itself was cold enough to make her fingers ache. The roof of the *Laplacian Express* reflected all the changing colours of the twilight. Thick pink and fragile lilac. Mirrored silver, slipping through the air like a serpent a hundred feet above the surface of Mars.

Alladice stopped on the roof of the next carriage and turned around to face her. He smiled. And he waited. Shai Laren spread her weight between her feet and opened up her fanblade – painting the air with a half-circle of gold-coloured metal. It would have been enough to scare off an opportunist, but Alladice only reached for the matt black baton at his hip. He thumbed the mechanism, and spikes of bare metal a foot and a half long speared out of either end.

Shai Laren swallowed hard and advanced. She reached out to the pneuma machina for resonance. Felt everything come into sharp focus. The desert sky like split goldstone. Whorls and whorls of stars. The roof of the train still warm from re-entry. The thrusters like a blast furnace underneath. Reflected light from the orbital array turned Alladice's face into sharp angles and deep shadow. She hopped the gap between the carriages and feinted forward, waited for him to lunge, then kicked off the roof of the train and cartwheeled over his head. Inverted in the air, she just had time to notice the natural stone archway racing out of the desert ahead before she had her back to it. Had to balance her weight carefully so that she didn't slip on landing.

A flash of metal, and Shai Laren swept her fanblade into a long arch in front of her to catch the blow. Nestled against her hindbrain, the pneuma machina ran numbers. The speed of the train. The pitch and incline. The height of the stone archway racing unseen out of the umber shadows behind her.

Duck. Now.

Her blade snapped closed with an audible crack. She rolled and pressed down against the hot silver of the train as the stone bridge whip-cracked past. She allowed her momentum to return her to a crouch, swept the blade open at Warden Alladice's ankles as he rose, then pivoted as he anticipated the blow and leapt. Adrenaline was a low roar in her blood, smothered by the steady stream of emotionless numbers pouring from the machine. Shai Laren rose and painted the air with a vertical arch of metal that sliced easily through the carbon weave of Alladice's staff. One of the telescopic spikes shuddered and collapsed in on itself. He thrust at her with the other.

The machine drank it in. Position of the blade, rotation in his arms. The tracery of her exoskeleton tightened a little in anticipation and she surrendered to it – sliding sideways over the curved roof of the train. Coming to a stop barely an inch from the dead drop into the desert.

Alladice threw the useless end of his staff at her, and ran. He was headed for the engine.

Shai twisted in mid-air, pulling her feet out of the way before Warden Alladice's half spear took them off. He had nowhere left to go now. A dozen feet of sharply curved engine housing was all that was left between them and the smokestack. Even from here, Shai could feel the blistering heat of it through her wrappings.

She landed, steadied her footing, and found him staring back at her. Realised what he was going to do halfway between when he acted and the last second that she could have stopped him. The machine made a snap calculation. She didn't have time to weigh up the pros and cons. She and Alladice swung themselves down into opposite sides of the driver's cabin at exactly the same moment.

As she straightened, the train's robotic pilot looked between them. Its face was featureless silver and couldn't register emotion. Not even when Alladice's spear split its head open from crown to collarbone. Smoke and coolant fluid sprayed over the bulkhead and sizzled down into the metal. Shai slid back as Alladice's spear slammed through the air where she had been and embedded itself in the console. The pneuma machina stabbed at her thoughts. No space to open her fanblade. *Best to unbalance him.* She grabbed his ankle with her free hand and pulled. When he sprawled backwards amongst the wreckage of the pilot, she half-opened her blade and stepped forwards. *No room here. We're at a disadvantage. Have to think of something else. Where the hell is Anselm?*

"Why are you doing this?" *Alladice is too sharp to fall for the distraction technique. Play for time.* "You want the Executive dead, I understand that, but why wait until now? Why not do it before Anselm and I even arrived? And why endanger the lives of everyone else on this train now that you've failed? How does that make you better than her?"

"Better than her?" Alladice laughed, wiping a long stripe of blood up the black sleeve of his body armour. "Stupid child. You have no idea what this is about. You think we care about Lascelles? About the *Queen of Heaven*? About anybody on this train?"

Shai's mind spun for a moment. "Who's 'we'?"

A nasty smile pulled at the corner of Alladice's

mouth. He brought up the tip of his spear. "If you'd lived," he said. "Perhaps you would have found out."

Her exoskeleton seized hold of her body, pushing her into a low crouch and bringing the closed shard of her fanblade up to block. Leaning her weight into her forward knee. Forcing him to step back.

"And when you're done with me," she said, "what will you do then? Anselm will not go down so easily."

Alladice repositioned his feet and cleaved down with another blow. Her exoskeleton constricted, splaying her feet out over the sizzling metal. Twisting her blade to hold him off. He backed up another step.

"I'll think of something," Alladice spat. "You think the two of you are the first members of your Church that I have killed?"

Shai's stomach turned to cold, clear water.

Stay calm. Get your feet back underneath you. Quickly. Raise your blade.

The force of the next strike reverberated in her arms. Muscles shivered with exertion. She made a show of trying to push herself up. Sliding forwards. Letting him retreat another pace.

Alladice's eyes flashed over his shoulder as his heel touched the edge of the cabin. "Such a clever girl," he said, smiling. "But not quite clever enough."

Before he could pull away from the edge, a hand reached out of the howling gale and plucked him into the open air. He hung suspended there, his face twisted with a mixture of fear and rage, the tattered remains of his cloak fraying in the wind. Then he was gone, rolling in a disordered mess underneath the thrusters of the *Laplacian Express*. A shadow burned down into the Martian sand.

Anselm swung down into the cabin and Shai Laren straightened up, wiping the sweat and dust off of her skin. "It's all right," she told him, looking down at the controls. "I'm almost sure I know how to fly this thing."

The *Laplacian Express* screeched and squirmed as it barrelled towards the canyon. Its thrusters burned blue and then white-hot as the ribbon of muscular silver jack-knifed and threatened to roll. Red sand spat into the thin atmosphere on every side. The last few carriages banked harder than the others. For several seconds before they righted themselves, the furnace of their underbelly was exposed to the air.

As the train finally ground to a shuddering halt, Anselm leaned out to watch it settle down into the desert. The air filled up with an eerie silence.

"A little bumpy, but we appear to have survived."

He dropped down into the sand. Shai stepped out of the other side of the cabin and took a slow pass around the engine. On the far side of the ravine the Martian capital glittered in the twilight, cupped in the crater of Solis Lacus. Aqueducts sloped gracefully down into the valley. High silver arches and sparkling lights. The whole city seemed silent from out here in the desert. Motionless. Its greatest skyscrapers outlined in a pale glow.

Shai turned her back on it and walked towards Anselm. "He said that it wasn't about the conference," she said. "That it was bigger than I could understand." And, when Anselm did not respond: "Warden Alladice, I mean."

Anselm nodded, watching as people from all across the Solar System climbed down out of the *Laplacian Express*.

Shai sighed. "What will happen if I leave the Church?"

"Difficult to say." He still wouldn't look at her. Even with his veil torn back from his face his expression was inscrutable. "Can't say I've known it to happen before. But the pneuma machina are precious, Shai. I can't imagine the keepers would simply allow you to walk away with one of them."

"And it can't be removed," she finished stonily, iridophores turning her skin as silvery as the city hanging in the heat haze. "At least, not without killing me."

Anselm nodded and drummed his fingers on his lips. His green eyes were murky and distant. Shai wasn't even certain that he was listening to her.

"And what will you do?" she asked, her teeth catching on the end of her tongue.

He drew a breath, and came into focus. "Well, if Alladice was part of some greater plan, as you say, then I shall need to find out who he was working with. Once I get these people to the Oc-ulus station, I'll start by running a background check on Alladice. I'm sure Executive Lascelles must have the information in her personal files. Then I'll interview the Mercurial. Find out about the man he murdered in the dining car. Try and work out if it's connected."

"And the trade conference? The prisoners on the *Queen of Heaven*? What is going to happen to them?"

Anselm's expression creased tight with frustration. "As I said, Shai, the matter is hardly our concern."

"And if I leave the Church?" she pressed. "If I walk away now and you become the first doula to lose one of his charges in…what? At least as long as you have been a member? What will the keepers make of that? Do you think *that* will be any of your concern, doula?"

The line of his mouth set hard. "You are playing a dangerous game, you realise that?"

She held his gaze and her ground, and waited for him to make his choice.

"Fine," Anselm sighed. "I will speak to Executive Lascelles and see if a compromise is at all possible. It's not entirely without precedent for the Church to intervene in certain matters of diplomacy. If you are so set on the idea, then perhaps you would like to carry out negotiations with the *Queen of Heaven* yourself."

Shai nodded slowly. She unwound the wrappings from around her forearms and used them to bind up her headtresses. Tucked the stray edge across her face, obscuring everything but her eyes. She hopped back up into the driver's cabin.

"I'm certain that the Executive will listen to you, Anselm," she said. "The two of you seem to be old friends, after all. While you are discussing it, perhaps you can ask if she will lend me Serethi's services until the matter is resolved. If we are to carry out negotiations between the Executive and the prisoners, I will need all the help that I can get."

Caerwyn Allegra Hawksmoor is busy preparing for the inevitable collapse of Western civilisation from their adoptive home in North Wales. They also write stories that have been published in *Beneath Ceaseless Skies* and *Interzone* #250, hang around on the dark and strange fringes of Facebook, and attempt to maintain a blog at www.hawksmoorsbazaar.net.

CHRISTIEN GHOLSON
THE SPIN OF STARS

ILLUSTRATED BY RICHARD WAGNER

The high desert night stretches out on all sides of the Jeep. Beyond the limits of the headlights, I can feel how the dark space curves away from the earth, folds in on itself, over and over, producing the billion stars that move across my windshield. There are moments, bumping over this dirt road, when I can feel the Pleiades star cluster above me; hundreds of stars spinning, keeping time. Real time – where past and future twist around each other; where beginnings and endings converge…

Exactly forty-six years ago – November 18th, 1968 – I was thumbing a ride on the other side of this continent, a mile west of Archer, Florida, near the Gulf Coast, when the temperature dropped close to freezing. I had no coat, no clothes except what I was wearing, so I wrapped my sleeping bag around me, stuck my thumb out, and waited. A few cars passed, no takers. Who'd pick up someone wrapped in a sleeping bag? The sun went down, the stars came out, and the temperature

dropped even more. Scared I was going to die of exposure, I turned around, started to walk back into Archer – thinking I'd nurse a cup of coffee at the local gas station for as long as they'd let me before they closed – when a yellow Mustang pulled up beside me. The driver leaned across the front seat, rolled down the window, asked me where I was headed.

"Cedar Key."

A trucker who'd picked me up near the Georgia state line had told me that Cedar Key, a remote village on the Gulf Coast, was an easy place to live on next to nothing. "Fish your dinner during the day," he said. "Sleep on the sand at night." It sounded like a good place to hide out for a while.

I was on the run. Two weeks before, I had been standing in a line in my underwear inside White-hall, the army induction center in New York City, about to be shipped off to boot camp, and then Vietnam. I'd just finished going through the physical exam (turn your head, cough) when this army psychiatrist began pacing the hall, calling out: "Does anyone need counseling? Counseling anyone?"

Seriously? We were standing in our underwear, about to be processed into a war, and he wanted to counsel us? Everyone looked at him like he was out of his mind. What could he possibly say that would help? We were already fucked, our fate sealed. For a second I thought he was some nut who had wandered in off the street wearing an army officer costume. There were a lot of folks in costume on the streets of New York in the fall of '68.

Despite the dark absurdity of it, and for no apparent reason that I could fathom at the time, I found myself raising my hand and following the psychiatrist down another hall to his office. He sat down behind a large wooden desk, motioned for me to take the chair facing him. I sat down and he asked me a few questions about how I felt about the war. I was cold, scared, sitting there almost naked, with no clue as to why I'd volunteered for counseling. I opened my mouth and out poured confusion, terror. What did I know about the war? I was from Saugerties, a small town in the Hudson Valley. Like all those other boys standing in that pale pea-colored corridor, I had seen shots of the war on TV, and probably

like most of them, I had a gut feeling that it was all wrong, so wrong. I didn't want to kill anyone. I didn't want to be killed. I told him that I didn't even know what I wanted to do with my life, and now I was heading to a sure death in a war that made no sense…

When I finished, he closed his notebook, nodded to himself, thanked me for my candor, then told me that I could re-join the line. I stood up, confused. Wait, what? That's it? No words of wisdom, no magical advice? Dejected, I found my way back to the green corridor. We shuffled forward slowly for another half hour and then a private wandered down the hall, calling out my name. I stepped out of line and he handed me a piece of paper, told me where I could pick up my clothes. I stared down at the paper. I'd been categorized as 4-F: *Not qualified for any military service.* As I hurried down the hall, toward my clothes, toward freedom, I heard the psychiatrist call out behind me: "Counseling? Anyone need counseling?"

What the fuck had just happened?

I hitched out of New York that day, headed south, no idea where I was going, trying to get as far away from the induction center as possible. I was terrified that some mistake had been made, a bureaucratic snafu, and that any minute a couple of MPs were going to show up behind me, drag me by my heels back to Whitehall.

I jumped into the Mustang, the sleeping bag still wrapped around me. The driver chuckled at my get-up, then fiddled with the knobs of the heater. "I don't think I've ever needed heat in this car before tonight," he said. The air that came out of the vents smelled of rubber and cobwebs dipped in coolant.

He drove slowly, leisurely, slumped low in his seat, one wrist at the top of the wheel, turning the dial of the radio with his other hand, looking for a station without static. Nothing satisfied him and he eventually snapped the radio off, turned to me.

"When I got home from Nam I hitched across the whole country," he said. "There's nothing like that freedom. You know what I'm talking about?"

I nodded. I had no idea what he was talking about. Freedom? What was that? I was a work-ing class kid who hadn't formulated any plan of action about what to do about the draft. I knew no one who had burned a draft card; I knew no one who had fled to Canada. The older brother of a friend had come back a quadruple amputee and was stuck in the VA hospital in Albany, but because I never saw him after he came back, it was just a story, distant, unreal. So I had used the time-honored method of dealing with any problem: I ignored it until it was too late. And yet I had still gotten out of it. How was that fair? Why had I escaped and not the guy sitting next to me, driving the Mustang?

....

"Freedom." I say it out loud, inside the Jeep driving across this high desert. It still has a taste as strange as it had back then. I remember how I had had the urge to confess to the driver, tell him what had happened to me at Whitehall. Why? I think I had wanted him to be enraged, scream at me. Back then, I was seeking absolution, to be released from the responsibility of my strange luck.

....

"I love it out here," the vet said. "This is a special land, strange land. My people come from these forests a long way back." He looked over at me: "I'm part Seminole." Then he winked. "People think all the Seminole were deported to Oklahoma, but the truth is that some headed down to the Everglades, and some mixed with runaway slaves. There's folks living so far back in there you gotta walk back two or three hundred years just to find 'em."

Another fifteen minutes down the road and he pulled to the shoulder. We were nowhere, dark pine forest on either side of the road.

"What's going on?"

"This is where we part ways," he said. "I'm heading to see a lady and she's not expecting you, so I got to let you out here. It's the best place to bed down between here and the Key." He pointed past me, at a dirt road that led into the forest. "If you follow that road there you'll find Dorry's Christmas Tree Farm."

I nodded like I understood; like it was the most natural thing in the world to get out of that car in the middle of Florida in the dark. Since crossing into The South, I'd done a lot of walking along the edge of swamps and forests hung with Spanish moss, waiting for a ride, and I'd gathered a litany of horrors in my head of what could possibly be back in those trees: roaches with huge octagonal heads and wings; snakes large enough to swallow an alligator whole; and the ubiquitous shadows that were not shadows, moving slowly, languidly, just out of sight, waiting, watching, tracking my every move. And now I was about to walk into one of those creepy forests in the dark, no light to guide me?

"Best night of sleep you'll ever have is under them pine needles in the tree farm," the driver said. "Just head up the dirt road and jump the gate. Moon's bright enough tonight, you'll find your way easy. Needles'll keep you warm."

"Are there swamps back there?"

He chuckled. "Keep to the tree farm and you'll be okay."

I found the Christmas tree farm – three acres of six foot trees growing in straight rows –quickly rolled out my bag and slid inside. In less than five minutes I was shaking so hard from the cold that I went hunting for brush to burn. I kicked a little pit into the dirt road, dumped in the twigs I'd found, and began working through a matchbook I'd picked up in a diner on Route 17, just south of Jacksonville. What tiny flames I ended up coaxing from the twigs wasn't enough to warm even the tips of my fingers, so in desperation I tore a post loose from the Christmas tree farm fence, dropped it on top of the smoldering brush.

That did the trick.

I don't know how many hours I spent by that fire, slowly feeding the post into the flames, before the old man appeared out of the dark. I didn't see him until he was right on me, standing on the other side of the fire pit. I saw the shoes first – old things, cracked, soles peeling from the leather – and I fell back onto the dirt, too shocked to make a sound. His face was heavily lined, gaunt; hands in the pockets of a huge, oversized down coat.

"You're trespassing," he said, then grinned. There were no teeth in his head. "Ain't my land, so I guess I'm trespassing, too."

He pulled a fifth of blackberry schnapps out of his coat, uncapped it, drank, and then held it out over the fire pit towards me. I struggled to my feet, shook my head.

"Go on," he said. "Warm you up."

I was cold. Against my better judgment, I took the bottle and drank. It was horribly sweet, burned going down. I handed the bottle back and he finished it off. It didn't make me any warmer.

"Old Man Dorry will be a bit put out tomorrow," he said, "you having burned his fence up." He grinned again, the inside of his mouth a dark hole. "He'll live. But you should come with me. I'll take you back to my place. They won't find you there."

He tossed the empty bottle into the darkness, turned, and walked down the dirt road, deeper into the forest. I stayed where I was. I wasn't going anywhere with some old man who'd just appeared out of the dark. Especially not further into those pines. He stopped, squinted up at the half-moon, and then glanced back at me.

"The Dorrys are bastards," he said. "Or can be, when it comes to this little shit farm. It's all they got."

I didn't budge.

"They got dogs," he added. "And they're not afraid to use 'em."

I had to decide between this toothless guy and the supposedly angry Dorry family with vicious dogs? The old man was tall, skinny, and frail, and I was pretty sure I could take him if it came to that, so I stepped over the fire, and walked about a half a mile down the road with him, to a huge white station wagon glowing blue in the moonlight.

The old man drove and drove, winding deeper into the pines – turning left, then right, right, then left, down dirt road after nameless dirt road – babbling on and on about the Dorrys and how they had stolen his land, land given to his family by the Spanish crown hundreds of years ago. When he'd finally exhausted his rant he pulled out a pack of Pall Malls, lit one up, and offered me one.

Eventually we turned onto a grass track, barely wide enough to fit the wagon, and parked in front of a small cinderblock house surrounded by huge live oaks. He cut the headlights, asked if I noticed anything strange about the place, then answered his own question before I could open my mouth.

"No dogs coming out to greet us," he said. "Know why?"

I shook my head.

"My Abuela don't abide dogs," he said. "They never tire of spooking round her – can't stop barking. Still, dangerous to live this far out without dogs, you're probably thinking. But I got spells that keep most folks out. Abby's spells. Mostly use 'em to keep the Dorrys from finding us."

He got out of the wagon, lit another cigarette, and offered me another. "I'll take you to see Abby in a few," he said. "She lives out back."

Spells?

"No dogs," he repeated, then shook his head and laughed. "Who'd believe?"

....

There were so many years when I ran, hid from what had happened to me. When I finally settled down, went to school, I became a psychologist, fascinated by trauma, any kind of trauma: childhood abuse, rape, war. Of course, over time I became consumed with war trauma – the neuroscience of it – what it does to the brain, the body – how to help give vets the tools to live, truly live, again.

There was a time when I worked exclusively with Vietnam vets at a VA hospital in Denver. Did I help anyone? Yes. No. There were small successes. As with all healing, the small victories had more to do with the vets themselves than anything I contributed.

That was a long time ago. A marriage fell apart. My wife and daughter drifted away into another man's family (ah, physician, heal thyself). I left the field. Over time, I found that there was something deeper calling out to me: the connections between all things, and how those connections play a part in healing.

....

Inside the cinderblock house, the old man lit a kerosene lamp, placed it on a flimsy fold-out card table next to a steel army cot. The dim light flickered on a potbellied wood stove in the corner, and a few cardboard boxes filled with empty bottles scattered around the cot. I stood near the door, watched the old man feed twigs and yellowed newspaper into the stove.

"I used to live out back with Abby, on and off," he said, shutting the stove's iron door and staring at the tiny flames through the smoky glass porthole. "Bigger place than this cold hole. But

I had to take her place apart for cash when she couldn't live there no more." He looked over his shoulder at me, pointed at the cot. "Sit on the bed if you want. Take a load off."

I kept standing. He shrugged, struggled to his feet, and started rummaging through one of the boxes at the end of the cot, pulling out a couple of empties, holding them up to the dim light, grunting, dropping them back in the box.

"I always leave some in a few bottles for nights just like this," he said.

When he found a bottle that still had about two or three swallows left, he sat down on the edge of the cot, unscrewed the cap, and drank. He held out the bottle, offered me the last swallow. I declined. He shrugged, tipped the bottle back, and finished it off.

"Abby's not like she once was," he said, wiping his mouth with the back of his hand. "She's been shifting back these last years. Getting more like *them*, you know, less like *us*."

I had no idea what he was talking about. I nodded.

"This is no place for her now," he said. "I want to get her out to the river, but she's so big…"

He stared at the empty bottle for a second, then got up again, went fishing in the same box for some more booze. Finding nothing, he looked around the room, eyes desperate. Then he snapped his fingers, rushed past me, flung open the door, and lurched out into the night. I reluctantly followed, watched him fumble through the station wagon, grunting and swearing. When it was clear he wasn't going to find any bottles in the car, he groaned, dropped to his knees, and began to cry.

I crouched next to him. "Let's go back inside."

He draped an arm over my shoulder. "I couldn't help Abby alone, you know." His breath was nicotine, alcohol, fish rot. "That's why she told me to come get you."

I led him back into the house, plopped him back onto his cot. I knew the routine. I'd led my drunk father back to his bed in the middle of the night hundreds of times during my childhood, talking him through every clumsy step – while my mother and older sisters slept on, having gone through the same routine themselves for years, long over the need to help him anymore.

"I know what she's done, what she's capable of," the old man said, "but once I'm gone, she'll be stuck out back alone, forever."

"What she's done?"

"Always testing," he said. "Poking in and out of…everything." He looked at me with blood-shot eyes, full of fear, his voice dropping to a whisper: "The way she touches, you know? She gets inside you…"

Whatever he was trying to say to me, I didn't want to hear it. I busied myself at the stove, tried to coax more flame from the wood, but it was useless, the wood inside was already half-charred.

"God knows I tried to leave," he said, his voice still a whisper. "Made it out for a number of years, but I always end up back here. She calls me back, somehow. It's like a dog whistle only I can hear, sound below hearing, words below regular thinking altogether. I thought I was the one who decided to come back, but that's not true, is it?"

I closed the stove door, stared at the worthless smoke curling against the glass.

"She's all I ever had," he said. "It's just been me and Abby, my whole life. What can I do? I have to help her."

I thought of the place where my father's mother had ended up: cracked, white plaster halls; the smell of boiled cabbage, piss, and bleach in the air; shriveled men and women in wheelchairs, drooling at ghosts. Her hands shook, her head shook; her brain completely gone from drink. Did she ever realize where she was? I hope not.

"Don't you have somewhere you could take her?" I said.

"There's no one left in my family," the old man said, "but she's still got kin on the other side." He sniffled, wiped his nose with a dark, stained handkerchief he pulled from his coat.

"Where?"

"South of here, Crystal River way."

He suddenly stood up, as if he'd heard a sound outside the door, then looked around the room, confused. I knew the look. He'd blanked out, didn't know where he was, who I was. My father did it all the time when I was leading him back to his bed.

"You drove me here," I said, talking him through it. "From Dorry's Christmas tree farm." He still looked confused. "You were talking about your grandmother," I added. "Abby."

Recognition came back into his eyes and he nodded, fished inside his coat, pulled out his pack of Pall Malls. "Christ, what she's done to me," he repeated. "I need her gone."

Hands shaking, he lit a cigarette and inhaled deeply, then moved past me, opened the door, and stepped outside, exhaling smoke into the cold night air.

"Let's do this."

....

The desert road ends at the entrance to a canyon that has no name. I leave the Jeep behind, move out on a trail that cuts through low shadows of black brush and scrub juniper. I can feel the boulders, the sandstone walls, up ahead. The faces of some of those other poor bastards who were standing in line with me forty-six years ago in Whitehall follow me into the canyon. Statistics say that many of them made it back. But many, many more killed themselves after they came home. Some of those suicides were friends of mine.

I can feel the ones who are still alive out there, too. New vets – back from Iraq and Afghanistan and god knows where else. Some are standing at a bedroom window right now, chain-smoking, staring up at the same stars, unable to shake the things they saw – and did.

I can feel their children; abandoned, lost. My own daughter among them – a young woman I barely know.

....

I followed the old man to the rear of the block house, watched him rummage through a pile of junk until he pulled out a torn tarp and a tattered burlap bag full of rope. Then we were on the move again, down a path through a thick stand of pines, emerging into a grassy clearing, with a small, man-made pond in the center. The old man walked up to the edge of the pond and something broke the water's surface: the back of a large creature – smooth, glistening in the moonlight.

I froze at the tree line.

"I've brought the boy, Abby," the old man said to the thing in the water. "He was exactly where you said he'd be."

He turned, beckoned me forward with a long index finger. I stood there for a few seconds,

sleeping bag still wrapped around my shoulders, heart pounding, eyes darting across the clearing, looking for an escape, seeing nothing but dark forest that stretched for miles on all sides. Where was I going to go? I *had* to move forward. There was nothing to do but shuffle slowly across the grass, towards the old man.

A large, whiskered snout lifted out of the water, and two small eyes set in an immense face stared up at me. The creature in the pond was a manatee. I said it inside my head, just to keep myself sane: *this old man thinks his grandmother is a manatee.* My next thought was: how had this frail old man captured a manatee, carried it here to this tiny pond in the middle of nowhere? He could barely lift a cigarette to his lips without shaking.

"She didn't always look like this," the old man said to me. "Looked like everyone's grandma when I was young, but she's been slipping back these last few years." He looked down at the creature. "Isn't that right, Abby?"

The dark eyes continued to study me.

"She's been in the family since Spanish times," the old man continued. "One of their soldiers got lost and Abby saved him. He thought she was a mermaid." He shook his head and repeated the word to himself, as if it was the most absurd thing in the world: "A fucking mermaid."

I felt something move around inside me: a shadow, a question; worming into my heart, my brain, down my spine; exploring, tasting. And then there was a voice, an old woman's voice, in my head: "We watched them wander through the swamp for days, slapping at mosquitoes, stumbling around. They never knew where they were, what they were, what I was…"

Through the terror, there was fascination – what had I stumbled on? I felt as if someone had just told me that they had the power to show me my own death. How could I say no?

"It's gonna be pretty cold once we get you out of there," the old man said to the creature, spreading the tarp out on the grass at our feet. Then he placed two of the rope ends in my hands: "Hold on to these. I need to get the rest under her." And with that, he slid out of his coat and jumped into the water.

I watched him disappear beneath the surface, immobile, the old woman's voice still echoing around inside me. A few seconds later he miraculously appeared on the other side of the creature, gasping for breath, his face and hair dark with mud, and tossed his end of the ropes over the manatee's back, towards me.

"Grab 'em, grab 'em!"

I grabbed the ropes, held tight, while the old guy scrambled up onto the grass on the opposite side of the pond. He stretched out on his stomach, lungs heaving, and began to sob again.

"What is *wrong* with you?" the creature hissed. The voice was not inside my head. It was outside. It was real. Real? The idea of *real* suddenly meant nothing at all.

The old man rolled onto his back, wiped his eyes with the back of a muddy hand. "How the hell am I gonna get you outta there when I can barely pull myself out?"

"Has everything I've ever taught you been completely erased by all that rotgut you drink?" the creature said.

The old man struggled to his feet, hair dripping, clothes clinging to his skin. "What you ask, Abby, what you've always asked, it's—"

The creature cut him off. "If you didn't always feel so sorry for yourself and drink so goddamn much you would remember that there are always forces at play, distant forces that can be harnessed. The spin of stars, the movement of planets – all have played their part in sculpting your worthless muscles and bones. Make the connections, boy! That's where you'll find your power! I'm already doing my part. You do yours."

The old man shuffled around the pond, stood next to me, his eyes sad, full of shame. "Okay, let's see if we can pull her out."

The creature angrily slapped the water with her tail. "Don't *see* if you can do it. Do it!"

We pulled and pulled, and the great body slowly rose out of the water, slid up and over the pond's edge, onto the tarp. How we did this, I am only just now beginning to understand.

We dragged the tarp across the clearing, through the pines, past the block house. When we reached the station wagon, the old man let down the back hatch and stared into the back, then glanced at the creature, his eyes full of confusion. He had gone blank again.

"You've gone and got me this far," the creature said to the old man, "and don't have a clue as to how to get me inside the car, do you?"

So far the creature had spoken out loud only to the old man and I wanted it to stay that way. Every time she spoke, I felt like something was strangling my breath, pins and needles in my arms and legs. But I desperately wanted to get rid of the creature, to be done with it, so I said that I'd seen planks behind the house and hustled off to find them.

Her voice – harsh, painful, tearing loose something deep inside me – followed me into the darkness: "You see what I have to put up with! It's been this way for five hundred years!"

....

The sandstone in this canyon is older than some of the starlight above. A language has evolved, is continually evolving, between stone and star, and this language has left an imprint on our muscle, bone. This language marks time, real time. I have been listening for it for years and years, but tonight – *tonight* – I can finally hear it.

What does it mean to heal an individual? Is that even possible? It has taken me so long to understand that the practice of healing one person means bringing the surrounding community into balance with the land, the sky, the planets and constellations above. There are only connections: the language of stone and star in the bones. This language pulls me deeper into the canyon.

....

The old man and I made a flimsy ramp and slowly pulled the creature up into the back of the wagon. All the while the manatee scolded the old man – for the pain caused, for his stupidity, for his drunkenness – and the old man apologized to her – for the cold, for the tightness of the ropes, for his weakness, for everything. We couldn't get her all the way in, so we had to leave her tail hanging off the back of the open hatch, which led to more scolding and apologizing. In the end, it took longer to pull the creature into that car than it had to drag her out of the pond and through the pines.

When we were out on the open road, the old man started to cry again. He looked into the rearview mirror, tears rolling down his face, lips quivering. "Abby? I'm gonna miss you. I just want you to know that."

"You're just saying that because you want me to say it back," the creature said, her voice harsh, vicious. "And none of it will be true."

The old man let out a sob. "But we *came* from you!"

"Stop your sniveling," the creature said. "Have some strength for once."

The old man went for his Pall Malls and chain-smoked for the next twenty minutes in silence. Eventually he turned off the road, onto a muddy track that led to an old wooden dock that jutted out into a black, moonlit river. He stopped in front of the dock, put the car in park.

"There it is, Abby, The Suwannee," he said. "You're almost home."

"You forgot the planks to get me out," the creature said.

The old man shook his head, hissing what sounded like "this is it, this is it, this is it" for a good half-minute before he finally twisted around in his seat and faced the creature. "Goddamnit, old woman," he screamed, "can't you see *this is it*! We'll never see each other again! Why do you always have to make things so goddamn hard!"

"Maybe we can turn around, back down to the end of the dock," I suggested. "Pull her out from there." I needed that creature gone.

The old man rested his forehead against the wheel. "You're not helping."

"He *is* helping," the creature said. "That's always been your problem: stubborn as your mother, your grandfather, your great-grandfather – all of them, all the way back. None of you ever truly listened to me."

The old man looked at me, bloodshot eyes full of rage. "You want me to drive onto the dock?!" he screamed. "You want me to drive onto the dock?!" He pressed one foot down on the brake, the other on the gas, then rammed the stick into drive. The tired, old engine whined, and the car fishtailed, back tires squealing, churning up mud.

"Stop these hysterics!" the creature shouted above the engine noise.

"You wanna go?!" the old man screamed into the rearview mirror. "Well, we'll all go, then! That make you happy?!"

I threw myself out the door, into the cold mud, and watched as the station wagon shot onto the dock. The old wood groaned, trying to hold up the car with the manatee inside it, but the weight was too much and the pilings buckled just as the station wagon reached the end of the dock.

I struggled to my feet, stared at the eerie sight of the station wagon's head and taillights glowing beneath the water, showing the outline of the car, sinking. The lights went out within seconds and I was left standing there in the darkness, paralyzed by the sound of the last air bubbles rising from the car, fizzing out on the surface of the water. Immobilized by fear – fear of the old man drowning, fear of diving in the water to help him – I stood there until the sound of the bubbles finally stopped and a terrifying silence enveloped the river.

That was when the manatee surfaced, ten feet from the bank. Her small, black eyes focused on me for a few seconds – a dark question, eating a hole through me – then she slipped quietly back below the water and was gone.

....

I've got a fire going in a narrow strip of canyon. Shadows of the surrounding boulders flicker against the rock walls. I sing to the cold light of the Pleiades cluster straight above me – flickering in and out of existence – and to the stones around me – flickering in and out of existence.

My voice echoes off stone, folds in on itself, sounding like many voices at once, a chorus of all the different lives I have led over the last forty-six years, rising up into the night. It is a song that contains star-clouds, army psychiatrists, sandstone, wind and water, Vietnam vets, the orbit of planets around each other, drunk fathers, and manatees that are not manatees. It is a song that I am making up as I go along. It is a song that was written long before I was born.

I can feel it now. The song is beginning to draw something from the shadows – something haunted, strangely beautiful – toward the edge of the firelight.

Christien Gholson is the author of the novel *A Fish Trapped Inside the Wind*, and a book of linked fictions *On the Side of the Crow*. He spent a part of his childhood in North Florida, near the St John's River, encountering many beautiful (and dangerous) creatures while roaming through the backwater swamps. He now lives with both the living and the dead in New Mexico, where the mountain ranges move this way and that, according to the light. Visit him online at christiengholson.blogspot.com.

COLD TURKEY

CAROLE JOHNSTONE

SHORTLISTED FOR A 2015 BRITISH FANTASY AWARD: "BEST NOVELLA"

VERY FEW PAPERBACKS LEFT!

TTA NOVELLAS 3

Wraparound cover art by Warwick Fraser-Coombe

Buy Cold Turkey for £10 or subscribe to five TTA Novellas for just £30, free postage worldwide. Visit our website for more information: ttapress.com/shop/

BOOK ZONE

**THE LONG WAY TO A SMALL
ANGRY PLANET**
Becky Chambers
Hodder & Stoughton hb, 416pp, £18.99

BECKY CHAMBERS
THE LONG WAY TO THE FUTURE

REVIEW AND INTERVIEW BY SHAUN GREEN

Life's rarely dull for Ashby, captain of the independent starship *Wayfarer*, but it's about to get tougher. Not because of the work, though contracting on bottom-tier subspace tunnelling jobs is an inherently risky proposition. Not because of his crew, even when unproven clerks are added to an already volatile cocktail of vigorous personalities. It's not even because he has to keep his romantic liaisons a secret from the galaxy at large. It's because he's about to take a contract which seems too good to be true. History suggests how that might pan out.

The Long Way to a Small Angry Planet kicks off in a traditional manner for space operatic adventure in an unfamiliar setting: it takes a character who has left her old life behind, in this case *Wayfarer*'s new clerk Rosemary, and lets the reader see through her eyes. From such a humble beginning we're introduced to a professional but good-hearted captain, a misanthrope who resents Rosemary's presence and provides early conflict, and the rest of a cast of colourful characters who share lives aboard a ramshackle but deeply-loved starship. If this already sounds familiar just wait until you meet Kizzy, the ship's "mech tech", who is so transparently a spin on *Firefly*'s Kayleigh that it's difficult to visualise the former as anything other than a slightly sterner Jewel Staite.

Fortunately Chambers' novel carries you along with enough charm and confidence to quickly dissipate any sense of over-familiarity. Moments of humour, springing organically from inter-actions between characters, play a part in this. They also serve to establish the *Wayfarer*'s crew as a living, breathing family of companions. *The Long Way to a Small, Angry Planet* is so intently focused on its core cast that it would fall flat if any of them fell short. They do not: each possesses a private life, with their own concerns, desires and relationships with other crew members. They're also a largely sympathetic bunch and it's a pleasure to spend time in their company.

The wider setting is also entertaining. As familiar as many aspects of it are, it does reframe many clichés in interesting ways. Humans are a minor species in the Galactic Commons but unlike, say, the Terrans of David Brin's *Uplift* novels, there is no 'human exceptionalism' to elevate them. They're just one species amongst many others and there is nothing much special about them – except their *dreadful* sense of smell. Meanwhile the Aandrisk, a reptilian species of which *Wayfarer*'s pilot is a member, are among the most interesting aliens present, and their unique approaches to interpersonal relationships, physical contact and child rearing are explored in contrast to human mores.

Over the course of the novel a number of diversionary sub-quests are undertaken, each of them conveniently introducing us to some social or political concept and piece of character backstory. These are never unwelcome but, on reflection, they are clearly rather obvious world-building asides. There's also one alien species whose veneer of inscrutable threat is more or less shattered as soon as we see things from their perspective.

Despite such qualms, and its occasionally obvious sources of inspiration, *The Long Way to a Small, Angry Planet* is a tremendously entertaining and assured debut, replete with moments of warmth, excitement and humour, and I'd read more in a heartbeat.

Your novel's humour and warmth stands out against the horror and cruelty that is inherent in its setting. How conscious was this juxtaposition, and was it a reaction to other SF works?

This is a broad comment with plenty of exceptions, but there has been a general trend in SF toward futures that suck, which makes total sense. Out in the real world, we're facing human-made problems on a planetary scale. That's not something we've ever had to do before, and it is freaking us out. We have no idea how to fix our environment or our social systems, or how we're supposed to overcome messes centuries in the making. Our contemporary stories largely reflect those fears, and that's healthy. But it's also important to look beyond all that and imagine far futures where things have gotten better. We need something to aim for, or else there's no point to the present. I thought about that a lot when I sat down to write this thing.

So, in my book, humanity screwed up. We broke the planet, and the galactic community that picked us up and dusted us off is far from utopian. But we're still here, and we have each other. We have family and love and worlds to explore. We have fun, despite it all. A lot of SF is focused on survival. I wanted to focus instead on the things that make survival worth the effort.

And these things are friend-ship, family and home – which seems a very close focus in contrast to the galaxy-span-ning plot that's largely hap-pening in the background?

That was done very intentionally. I spent much of my childhood imagining myself in the United Federation of Planets, or hanging out on Tatooine, but I never saw myself as one of the heroes there.

"My goal was to take a space opera and flip the camera around. There are indeed big, big things going on, but that's the background noise"

I wanted to know what it was like to just live there. I wanted to know where the people walking through the background of the shuttleport were off to. Because for most of us, the world is not a place of thrill-ing battles and political intrigue. Those are things happening some-where far away, things we hear about on the news while we're eat-ing dinner and texting our friends. My goal with *The Long Way* was to take a space opera and flip the camera around. There are indeed big, big things going on, but that's the background noise this time. What's up front is something I wanted average Joes and Janes to relate to. This is a future where space is for everybody.

***The Long Way* is notable for not placing space-age human-ity centre stage. What drove your idea that human beings are not the most special snow-flakes in all spacetime?**

In short, Carl Sagan. I devoured everything my local library had of his after the film adaptation of

Contact blew my little middle-school brain wide open. *Pale Blue Dot* is my compass in most things. I subscribe to the belief that we're not going to progress as a species until we own up to the fact that we're not the end-all-be-all (which, counterintuitively, makes us pretty wonderful).

There's a lot of SF in which we're not the highest rung on the galactic ladder, but those stories often make us prove our worth through some sort of heroics – a military conquest, or a scientific achievement. Either we beat the aliens at their own game, or we turn out to be the only ones who can save the galaxy (or both). I love a lot of stories that follow those patterns, but we could do with some alternatives, too. I don't think victory and glory are the highest forms of relevance, I don't think resource or territory competition is an inevitability, and I don't think we need to be the best in order to matter. There are a lot of different human cultures on display in *The Long Way*, and some of them have stuck with old habits. But the ones who have travelled the furthest are the ones who ate some humble pie and mellowed out.

It's not just humanity either, is it? I'm thinking here of the Aandrisk, as well as the galaxy's one-time mollusc empire.

I should write a series called Mol-lusc Empire. But yes, exactly. This isn't a hard-and-fast rule in the book, but generally, species who learn to cooperate – or at the very least, coexist – do better in the long run. The community they all belong to is largely based in the idea of sharing the wealth, and there is some old, old colonial bad blood that nobody likes dredging up. You're not going to be particu-larly welcome if you come in play-ing the Superior Species card.

The Long Way began public life as a Kickstarter campaign back in 2012, and Hodder & Stoughton picked it up after editor Anne Perry read a copy. How did you get from a small crowdsourced campaign to a book arriving in her hands? Did you find that word of mouth took off, or are you secretly a very canny publicist?

I'm an atrocious publicist, and the whole to-do was dumb luck more than anything. I met Anne at a Worldcon party last summer. I was on staff at The Mary Sue at the time; Anne (together with Jared Shurin) was up for the Hugo for Best Fanzine. We didn't meet as editor and author. We met as two people who wrote stuff online. I had no idea she was in publishing until after the fact, and since I am brilliant at self-promotion, I didn't think to mention that I had written a book. Jared contacted me a few months later, after he'd found the book on his own. I am safely assuming he handed it off to Anne. She and I hadn't been in touch since the con when she popped the publishing question. I'm still kind of baffled by it.

There's a resilient idea in SF that new writers must cut their teeth publishing short fiction before moving on to a novel. You buck that trend. Any comments regarding your own trajectory, or the field in general?

I love reading short fiction. I hate writing it. It took me a long time to come to terms with that, because yeah, you're supposed to start small and work your way up. I tried, I really did. At first, I thought I needed more practice (which was true – the stack of rejection letters I acquired was justly deserved). After a while, though, I realised it wasn't my thing. Short fiction is a different craft than writing a novel.

"Short fiction is a different craft than writing a novel. I respect the hell out of it, and I'm in awe of the people who can do it well"

I respect the hell out of it, and I'm in awe of the people who can do it well. But writing a cohesive story in two thousand words is a whole different beast than writing one in a hundred thousand. I'm more at home with the latter. I like having room to spread things out. Once I decided to play to my strengths instead of following someone else's road map, my writing got a lot better.

That's an interesting remark, because I wondered if some parts of *The Long Way* were first written independently – they felt a little like a short story in their own rights. Visiting the Aandrisk homeworld, for example, or the scenes with the human survivalists on the *Pitch Black*esque moon. Was I wrong?

Nope, you're right on the money. I came up with the crew about ten years ago, when I was still in college. I wrote tons of stories about them, usually while travelling, and I had absolutely no idea

what to do with it all. It's a perfect example of why I don't do short fiction well. Though most of the chapters originated as little scenes I wrote in airports or on trains or whatever, none of them work independently. They were all feeding off of the big road map I had going on in my head – the politics, the technology, the relationships these people had with one another. Take that first chapter you mentioned. The trip to the Aandrisk homeworld is nothing but a photo of a family dinner if you don't have the larger context of mainstream cultural differences between Aandrisks and Humans, or who Rosemary and Sissix have been up to that point. That part stands on its own within the book, but it can't exist without the book. I think that's true for all of it.

This here is the traditional enquiry about sequels, or other future projects. Please tease us!

I'm working on a companion novel that falls alongside the later events of *The Long Way*. It follows two characters we've already seen a little bit of, but I can't go into too much detail, because it'd spoil things for people who haven't read the first book yet. But for those who have: You can find the characters in the chapter 'Staying, Leaving'. They are not *Wayfarer* crew members, though one could have been, had things gone differently.

Finally, how does it feel to share a name with a character from *Resident Evil*?

This is the first time in my life someone has pointed this out to me rather than the other way around. I hate to disappoint, but I do not typically carry first aid spray.

It pleases me to be the first. Becky, thanks very much for your time!

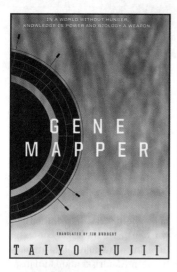

GENE MAPPER
Taiyo Fujii (translated by Jim Hubbert)
Haikasoru, 297pp, $14.99

Maureen Kincaid Speller

Translation is not a cheap business. Which makes me curious as to why Haikasoru thought it worth translating *Gene Mapper* for the English-language market when, to me at least, it doesn't really seem to be that good. The answer may lie somewhere in the novel's slightly confusing genesis: Fujii originally published a version of *Gene Mapper* as an e-book and it sold 10,000 copies. At this point Hayakawa Publishing, well-known as a publisher of science fiction in Japan, apparently contacted Fujii and asked for what one newspaper has described as "a full-length novel", suggesting that the original version was probably rather shorter. Subsequently, *Orbital Cloud*, Fujii's second novel, not yet available in English, won the 2014 Japan SF Grand Prize.

Here, I am caught on the horns of a dilemma. So far as I am aware, I have read no Japanese science fiction in translation, so I have no idea if *Gene Mapper* is typical of Japanese SF or whether the problems I have with it arise simply

from Fujii's being an inexperienced writer. I incline to the latter, and Fujii himself freely admits that he later signed up with a traditional publisher to benefit from editorial advice, so this review is conducted on that basis.

Mamoru Hayashida, the narrator of this story, is a gene mapper: that is, he is a designer programming the DNA of rice crops. The story is set in 2036 and crops are being "distilled'" from scratch in order to combat world hunger. My first difficulty arises here – it is remarkably difficult to get a sense of what it is Hayashida actually does. Whether this is because it is incredibly complicated or because Hayashida can't properly explain it isn't clear. Which is curious because, if there is one thing that Hayashida likes doing, it is explaining. His narrative is one long explanation of everything he sees, does, and uses (especially when it comes to software and augmented reality) to the point where the novel seems more like a speculative description of the future with a few shreds of plot gathered around it for modesty's sake than it does a full-blown novel. It does, though, make the failure to explain what Hayashida does seem far more obvious than it otherwise might have been.

Which suggests to me that Fujii himself is much more interested in showing how Hayashida and his colleagues use augmented reality than he is in telling the story. And indeed, in that newspaper interview, Fujii observes that "a world with augmented reality is a better place to live", in which case it would make sense to show how AR might work for someone living in the future.

But this is my second problem: Fujii's fascination with the trappings of the future threaten to overwhelm the plot, what there is of it. It flickers fitfully, like the light from the jellyfish genes that will become significant as things

progress. It is a simple enough story. Even in 2036 environmental activists are eager to put a stop to artificially produced crops, though in this instance they appear to have adopted bizarre measures to do so. It is up to Hayashida to figure out what is happening before his company's credibility is destroyed. This involves Hayashida travelling in person to the site, along with his colleague, the mysterious Takashi Kurokawa, headhunting a number of hacker types to help with research, and then, right on cue, being handed most of the answers on a virtual plate. We have, so to speak, been here before, many times.

Nonetheless, there is a certain attractive quality to Fujii's main characters. Dialogue is not among Fujii's core skills as a writer but every now and then something sparks on the page. Hayashida's relationship with Kurokawa, his putative mentor, is oddly charming, while his growing relationship with Shue Thep, the researcher overseeing the rice-growing project, is expressed in conversations that actually feel convincing, not least when she's complaining about a lack of equipment. The villains of the piece, however, look and sound like stock villains. We realise quickly that Hayashida and his friends are unlikely to come to any notable harm as they try to solve the mystery at hand.

Given that Fujii's primary interest lies in the way humans interface with technology, I hope he will in future address those issues more directly in his work and give his readers something richer to deal with, rather than simply bolting a flimsy plot onto lavish descriptions. That Fujii recognises the need for editorial advice and guidance seems to me to be a positive thing. Nonetheless, it is a shame that our first encounter with his writing must be with something that still seems strangely unfinished.

THE FIFTH DIMENSION
Martin Vopěnka (translated by Hana Sklenkova)
Barbican Press pb, 283pp, £8.99

Duncan Lunan

Like his central character, Martin Vopěnka studied maths and nuclear physics, then abandoned science until his interest was rekindled by Kip Thorne's book *Black Holes and Time Warps*. His first-person narrator Jakub Dohnal is a failed Czech businessman who signs up for an experiment involving a year's isolation, whose purpose he is not told, and for which he is allowed to take only one book. He will forfeit his large fee if he quits or reveals the details to anyone, but he tells his wife, who later tells a friend, and it makes no difference at all.

It would be easy to take this novel for SF, but despite the trappings the approach is mainstream. The only real question is, will he or won't he get the money? And the answer is ambiguous, not to say contradictory. Czech critics have compared Vopěnka's work to Kafka and to Milan Kundera, author of *The Unbearable Lightness of Being* – which doesn't mean this isn't heavy going.

The test, in a high-altitude bunker concealed in the mountains of Argentina, appears pointless. The site has lots of solar power and battery storage – like a fallout shelter, but with no airlock or decontamination; like a Mars simulation, but with no scientific workload, just routine physiological tests which could be done better at any high-altitude observatory. As a psychological study, Jakub's supposed isolation is a joke. He is first befriended by a llama, which is then shot by a visiting local. Fabian, the visitor, knows about the installation and is in touch with its American monitors – but he can't reveal its purpose, since he speaks only Spanish and Jakub only Czech and English (tick the Kafka box). Language isn't a problem with a Czech climbing party from whom Jakub conceals his nationality, overhearing that they're going to sacrifice their only woman member to a sun-god on a nearby mountain. Then the American monitors turn up, repeatedly, from Czechoslovakia, using their employers' travel facilities to subvert the experiment – one, Howard, to ensure Jakub stays put while he seduces Mrs Dohnal, the other, Denis, to blackmail Jakub himself into a homosexual affair (tick the Kundera box).

From the outset, Jakub is beset by paranormal visions. At first he can only watch his family through pyschometric contact, but by the same method he follows the climbers to their mountaintop altar and witnesses Veronika's ritual killing. He has no radio, so he can't call for help; he can't reveal himself to the subsequent search parties because that would contravene the experiment, hopelessly compromised though it is, whatever it is. By psychometric link to Fabian's village, he learns that the killers' leader has returned to erase any remaining evidence. Reading Thorne meanwhile,

Jakub concludes that not just gravity but paranormal communication, and ultimately all consciousness, occur in the fifth dimension of space-time (postulated by Einstein, detected by Eddington in 1919, and confirmed by Hubble images of gravitational lensing, though only black hole theory gets a mention here). The paranormal aspect would be familiar to Victorian readers as 'the fourth dimension', though that risks confusing it with time unless you specify 'fourth *spatial* dimension'. Since the evidence for five – at least – is nearly a century old, Vopěnka is in tune with modern physics.

To prove it all to himself, Jakub must follow Veronika's killers to prove their mountain-top altar matches his vision. It does, so it's all true. He achieves union with God through the fifth dimension (it takes two sentences), learns that his visions of events in Czechoslovakia weren't true after all (huh?), returns to the bunker and refuses to answer the door to a visitor, be it the killer, Fabian, Howard, Denis – he doesn't answer. A month later, he's continuing the experiment in isolation; the same day in Europe, Jakub's wife receives a letter from Denis saying he's been found dead, off-site, so she will receive only token payment.

So has God moved him to an alternative reality where he's still alive, his wife is still faithful and he'll be paid in full? Is he dead and doesn't know it? Is he alive but delusional, now at Denis's mercy? It's all so rushed at the end, at least in translation, that your guess is as good as mine. Tick 'deep philosophical significance'? If so, it escaped me. The last word in the book is Denis's surname, which turns out to be Pascal – a cynical comment that morality, religion and science are irrelevant at high altitude? Whatever you make of it, the box not to tick is the one marked 'SF'.

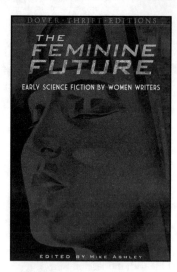

THE FEMININE FUTURE
Edited by Mike Ashley
Dover Thrift Editions pb, 228pp, $4.50

John Howard

For some forty years Mike Ashley has been one of the leading historians of science fiction, and especially of magazine sf. His books are indispensable. One reader remembers the teenage pleasure of discovering Ashley's *The History of the Science Fiction Magazine* (and yes, it did what it said on the covers of its four volumes). Beginning with something of their prehistory – before 1926 and *Amazing Stories* – Ashley researched, tabulated, and chronicled the rise and fall of science fiction publishing empires. They were publishing *something* that the readers clamoured for. In order for us to know what all this fuss was about – the stories – Ashley's *History* was also an anthology, and included fiction from the magazines and writers discussed. Thus it was that he brought rare treasures to light. Sometimes the gold was crude gilt, flaking easily. But they were pieces from the basement, many having been left there in the dark for half a century. They did things differently then. There was much glamour – and wonder.

During the first decade of this century Ashley revised and updated his *History*, which currently ends at 1980. The new iteration is improved but contains no stories; however, Ashley has remained busy as an anthologist. There is, luckily, no stopping him clambering up from the basement, bringing more forgotten stories out into the light.

The writers represented in the old *History* were overwhelmingly male, but there were female writers active in that SF era – and its prehistory. It is mainly this pre-*Amazing* world that Ashley opens up in *The Feminine Future*. We get fourteen stories, the oldest first published in 1873 and the latest in 1930. The original places of publication include *Argosy*, *The Black Cat*, *Science Wonder Quarterly*, and *Astounding Stories*. Ashley supplies a short biographical and thematic introduction to each story. It is noticeable how often the authors turned to writing in order to support family. The usually male protagonists are often obsessive inventors, making use of new technologies and discoveries – electricity is a favourite. There is much melodrama, and the atmosphere is often rather gothic; at the same time contrasts are drawn between the old (existing) world and a dawning new age (or future setting). And as is commonly observed about science fiction, much of the interest here lies not in any predictions made, but in what the stories say about the time they were written.

Among the more striking are these. In 'The Automaton Ear' (1873) by Florence McLandburgh it is theorised that sounds never completely die away, and can therefore be captured with the right equipment. The title is the plot with 'Ely's Automatic Housemaid' (1900) by Elizabeth Bellamy, but the machine is a robot in the modern sense, and not an android

as, say, the workers were to be in Čapek's *R.U.R.*

In Lillie Devereux Blake's 'A Divided Republic – An Allegory of the Future' (1887) women are denied the vote by Congress, and move *en masse* to Washington and Wyoming Territories, where at the time they were enfranchised. This is an amusing satire which makes a point or two before the inevitable reconciliation. 'Via the Hewitt Ray' (1930) is the only known story by M.F. Rupert. Set in the 1950s, the female narrator is a commercial pilot whose inventor father detects communications from another dimension, and decides to go there. She follows him into the three new dimensions or planes he finds. In the second women are in control, and have killed most men except a few retained for breeding purposes. Rupert illuminates a range of sometimes uncomfortable moralities.

'The Great Beast of Kafue' (1917) by Clotide Graves is set not long after the end of the Boer War, and involves Boer characters in a story told from their point of view. Following sensational newspaper reports of the sighting of a monstrous creature, a boy wants to hunt it down. His father stops him, extracting a vow never to kill the beast. He then explains why. This is an oddly moving story of loss and empathy that transcends humanity to involve other living – and feeling – creatures.

Summaries of all except two of the stories in *The Feminine Future* were included by E.F. Bleiler in *Science-Fiction: The Early Years* or *Science-Fiction: The Gernsback Years* (the two omitted presumably not meeting his criteria). So while none of these stories are previously unknown, they will, with one or two exceptions, still be difficult to find. Mike Ashley has performed another great service, and another piece of science fiction's past has been restored to view.

WINNER OF THE ARTHUR C. CLARKE AWARD 2013 FOR
DARK EDEN

CHRIS
BECKETT

MOTHER OF EDEN

'A rising star of British SF... Beckett should be on
the radar of anyone who professes concern for science
fiction as a literary form' Alastair Reynolds

MOTHER OF EDEN
Chris Beckett
Corvus hb, 468pp, £17.99

Juliet E. McKenna

Chris Beckett's *Dark Eden* won the 2013 Arthur C. Clarke Award and I was one of the judges choosing it. So I approached *Mother of Eden* with eager anticipation and acute apprehension. *Dark Eden* is one of the most original SF novels I've read in years. It was also complete in itself and that's rarer than it should be. Yes, like all the best fiction, *Dark Eden* leaves the reader wanting more, but could Beckett possibly deliver a second novel to equal it? Would *Mother of Eden* have the same impact for those already familiar with *Dark Eden*'s astonishing setting? Will new readers be left floundering?

In setting this story several generations later, Beckett addresses both concerns. Established and new readers alike pick their way through an unfamiliar scenario unfolding on this dark world lit by the bioluminescence of its intensely alien flora and fauna. We see new places and creatures, now the human population has expanded from that first settlement founded by stranded spacefarers into several distinct tribes. Each has its own

developing culture woven from half-remembered Earth traditions by people never intended to be colonists. Thus the claustrophobic atmosphere of the first book shifts to uneasy tension between the possibilities of this wider world and dangers of the unknown.

In these oral cultures, recapping the first book's events is woven into the narrative with more than simple reiteration. When Starlight Brooking and a group of relatives strike out from their small settlement founded by Jeff Redlantern, they find the Davidfolk of Veeklehouse have a very different view of the fratricidal strife that drove the first desperate wave of emigration from Circle Valley. The Davidfolk also have guards policing rules that Starlight and her family don't understand. While these travellers are not stupid, ignorance or naivety could prove costly.

As these Knee Tree Grounders try to navigate through unfamiliar concepts like trade with tokens rather than barter, some Johnfolk arrive from across the sea. They have their own version of events, perpetuating the original quarrel. They also have red metal and other trade goods which the Davidfolk covet. Technological advances on both sides of the sea are improving and complicating life on Eden. But that's as nothing to the fraught question of who possesses Gela's Ring, one of the few heirlooms from the original humans and now a token sought by all sides to prove they are the ones in the right.

Greenstone Johnson, the Headmanson from New Earth's distant shore, is entranced by Starlight and she accepts his offer to become his Housewoman, travelling to his unknown home. Except nothing is nearly as simple as it first appears. It's a good thing that Starlight is an accomplished chess player; part of this diaspora's common heritage. She finds herself thrust into another hierarchical

society, and one that's heavily, even violently, misogynistic. Is such a development inescapable? Is Beckett saying patriarchy is intrinsic to human nature? Or should the reader follow Jeff Redlantern's philosophy and concentrate on the here and now in this story rather than trying to decide if Eden is somehow meant to be a microcosm of our own world?

The narrative is ably carried by deceptively simple, skilful writing through the viewpoints of distinct characters. Their differing perspectives enrich and inform the reader's understanding, from Starlight to, among others, her sister Glitterfish, to Julie (another Knee Tree Grounder), to Greenstone, to the woman Quietstream who becomes Starlight's servant, to Lucy Johnson with her own reasons for wanting to see New Earth's Headmanson fall. We see how these small, limited societies are so powerfully shaped by the choices of forceful individuals. We see progress driven by the restless and curious, not the meekly content. We see prejudice learned by the biddable and wielded by the dominant. Which brings us to consider our own cultures. Every society is made up of individuals, after all, ultimately formed by personal decisions.

Such questions underpin but never overwhelm an enthralling and fast paced story. Beckett's facility with Eden's evolving language adds a further subtle dimension without ever compromising immediacy or readability. Very real peril, challenging, even unnerving surprises and tantalising questions continue to the final pages where the ending proves both satisfactory and yet in many ways inconclusive. But that's no criticism. It's the nature of history after all. Individuals' stories are only ever part of the ceaseless flow of events.

So Beckett more than meets the challenges of this second Eden novel, leaving me keen to read more.

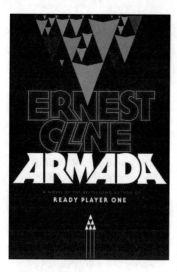

ARMADA
Ernest Cline
Century hb, 355pp, £12.99

Stephen Theaker

Zack Lightman's dad died in an explosion at a sewage treatment plant, and it made the papers so *everyone* knows. That was back in 1999. A bully called Douglas Knotcher once took the mickey about it, and got battered to a pulp after Zack went into a blind rage. He's been trying to live it down, but it hurts to miss his dad so much while finding his death so humiliating. His mum kept all his dad's stuff in boxes up in the attic. Zack watched his videos, played his games, and wore his jacket covered in high score patches.

A notebook he found there, back when he was ten, made him think his dad had lost it, and chapter two takes us through it. A four-page chronology begins with *Space War* in 1962 and *Star Trek* in 1966, then works its way through *Star Wars*, *Close Encounters*, *Ender's Game*, *Battlezone*, *Elite*, *The X-Files*, *Contact* and *Galaxy Quest*, to pick out a few. His dad thought they were all connected, part of a conspiracy controlled by the U.S.

military, preparing humanity for an alien invasion.

Now it's 2018. After Zack sees a Sobrukai Glaive Fighter streaking around outside his high school in Beaverton, Oregon, he thinks he might be cracking up too. It looks pretty cool, like the blade of a two-headed battle axe with a black prism sitting between its serrated wings, but it's from *Armada*, his favourite video game, created by Chaos Terrain, who, in a suspiciously *Watchmen*esque move, hired the best of the best to work on it, people like Gabe Newell, Shigeru Miyamoto, James Cameron, Peter Jackson, John Williams and Morgan Freeman.

The gamer plays a pilot, one of many defending Earth against an invading fleet of alien ships, controlled by anthropomorphic extraterrestrial squids from Tau Ceti. Players often complain about the unbalanced gameplay and the unbeatable missions (uh-oh!), like the one where the Disrupter, with its shields that drop for just three seconds, locks on to Earth and disables all the drones, but that hasn't harmed its popularity, and Zack, especially, and fortunately, isn't one to give up when the odds are against him.

There's a terrestrial spin-off where you pilot a mech, *Terra Firma*, and Zack plays it sometimes, but just so his pals will join him for the big *Armada* missions. That's his passion: it took years of daily practice to crack the top one hundred, a few months more to make the top ten, and now he's the sixth best player in the world. His handle is IronBeagle. (Later on, when an attractive young woman gets that it's a reference to *Snoopy vs the Red Baron* and *Iron Eagle*, he'll know she's the one.)

The alien ship he saw? Not a hallucination. An alien armada is on the way for real, and Earth

really does needs Zack to defend it. Just as he's about to wallop Douglas Knotcher with a tyre iron after another altercation, an Earth Defence Alliance shuttle arrives to scoop him up. There are more secrets in Zack's life than he could ever have guessed, and that life will be shorter than he could ever have ever imagined if his gaming skills aren't sufficient to meet the alien challenge.

This isn't a book that provoked strong feelings in me. It was entertaining enough in a three-star Hollywood sort of way: the author's previous book, *Ready Player One*, will soon be a Spielberg film, and this one has half a dozen roles into which you could slot a movie star. It might make a good film; it's not as if we're overwhelmed with outer-space action, and its conclusion, though a bit cheesy on the page, might still seem novel in cinemas.

The constant referencing of pop culture (a big part of *Ready Player One*'s popularity) feels a bit ingratiating, and even patronising: if your characters are going to talk about losing their goram shields and being out of frakkin' power, let us feel clever for recognising them (or at least like we've spent our television time wisely). Don't have another character name the shows, just in case we didn't get it.

Maybe this is aimed at younger readers, though they might wonder why this teenager has the cultural touchstones of a middle-aged man. Missing your dad is one thing, but he has apparently watched all the shows and played all the games it's taken me forty years to get through. That stuff dies down once Zack is out in space and it becomes a decent action adventure, but, even then, I'm not sure tipping your hat to *The Last Starfighter* makes it okay to nick its plot – even if this is in truth more of a *Phantom Menace*.

THE WATER KNIFE
Paolo Bacigalupi
Orbit hb, 384pp, £16.99

Paul Graham Raven

If you enjoyed the stark, violent catastrophism of *The Windup Girl*, you'll likely find much to enjoy about *The Water Knife*, though its apocalypse-in-progress (the ever-escalating drought in the southern US) is considerably closer to home in temporal terms. A stickler for taxonomy might argue that it's really a technothriller. One might also compare it to Sterling's *Heavy Weather*, which deals with a similar issue in a similar territory: Sterling is interested in showing us the sociotechnical systemicity of the problem, while Bacigalupi is interested in who survives the bottleneck, and how.

The world of *The Water Knife* is not one whose collapse might be prevented, or even managed. It might be escaped – but only by those who can buy their way into the sealed eco-systems of the arcologies, expensive life-rafts in a bone-dry sea. For everyone else, it's a Hobbesian life in the refugee favelas. A maguffin is hunted; dastardly deeds abound; threads are drawn together, or mercilessly snipped off; the pages turn swiftly.

It's an engaging and topical near-future novel, albeit one haunted by the same problematics regarding the depiction of sex and violence that animated *The Windup Girl*.

But the most chewy bit is the ending – so, spoiler-haters, get thee gone.

Still here? Good.

Bacigalupi seemingly has two projects in this novel; the first is to depict the escalation of drought conditions in the southern US, and present it as a function of history rather than an out-of-the-blue apocalypse. What impact this will have is uncertain; people have been narrating the rapacious thirst of California for as long as that state has existed. As with other manifestations of climate change, it's not that we don't know it's happening; it's that we all fail to make the connection between the despoilment of distant environments and the effortless fulfilment of our desires. While *The Water Knife* does a great job of dramatising resource conflict, the violence done by people to the world is overshadowed by the violence done by people to each other; the individualist dynamics of the technothriller cannot sustain what Tim Carmody calls "the systemic sublime", the epiphanic hit of conceptual breakthrough wherein the world is revealed as more complex than before.

Which brings us to his second project, namely to interrogate the morality of a dustbowl continent crawling with refugees. In a final-scene reversal reminiscent of a Sergio Leone movie, the maguffin – old water deeds issued to a Native American tribe two centuries before, the ultimate in what water law calls "senior rights" – is in the hands of the idealistic journalist who's just been through hell trying to find it. With these ancient bits of paper, she can put up a legal bulwark against the desertification of Arizona; she can hold back the tide, if only for a little while, by

playing the legislators and deal-makers at their own game.

But instead, Bacigalupi has her shot in the back by the refugee who'd unwittingly been carrying the thing. To her, the collapse of Arizona and beyond is a given; she knows that the inevitable can only ever be deferred, not prevented. Seeing a choice between deferring ecological collapse for many, or simply buying her own way out of its path, she chooses the latter – the same choice that the water knives made, but in miniature.

This feels less like an endorsement of market fetishism than an observation that market fetishism is a self-fulfilling prophecy: that the only thing that "trickles down" in such a system is an atrophy of collective values. Bacigalupi has done sufficient research to understand both the technological and the social dimensions of this particular arena of the climate wars, and the novel seems to me to argue that the window of opportunity on the social side is closing fast, if it isn't closed already – and that once it's closed, selfishness becomes the only rational survival strategy. Scarcity trumps morality, forever.

I very much believe that Bacigalupi shows us the worst of apocalypse and dystopia in hope of nudging us toward something better, no matter how slightly, but *The Water Knife* also admits of a more cynical reading: that a slow-motion civilisational car-crash is inevitable, and we'd be wise to jettison our bleeding hearts and activate our inner Gordon Gekko if we want to see out Babylon's last hurrah in comfort. That's an ugly reading, for sure – both of the book, and of the world – but these are ugly times, and the history of water in the southern US is uglier still. So enjoy this self-confessed "collapse porn" technothriller, but don't come to Bacigalupi in search of hope for a brighter future. That well's long dry already.

THREE MOMENTS OF AN EXPLOSION
China Miéville
Macmillan hb, 448pp, £18.99

Ian Hunter

I was thinking to myself recently: whatever happened to China Miéville? Author of some of my favourite, yet very different, novels of recent years such as *Kraken*, *The City and the City*, *Embassytown* and *Railsea*. I'd caught him at a few Edinburgh Book Festivals, and the last time I saw him inside one of their stuffy marquees he was promoting *Railsea*, although he had also just published a small, almost political, pamphlet or chapbook called 'London's Overthrow', his take on the real life of many Londoners in a time of austerity (and I'd urge you to hunt down a copy). But where was the next novel? Where? Well, there is one coming in 2016 called *The Census Taker* – and tantalising snippets are available now for you to hunt down.

In the meantime we have a collection called *Three Moments of an Explosion*. But be warned: these are perhaps stories, but not as you know them. For sure, there are obvious tales on offer here, and taken from many different sources such as *The Guardian*, *Granta* or *McSweeney's*, but there are also fragments. Four of the pieces were handouts by the Foundation for Art and Creative Technology in Liverpool to accompany a work called 'The New Death' so that should be enough of a warning to expect the unexpected. I'm reminded of hearing Ellen Datlow on a panel saying that sometimes she's promised a story from Neil Gaiman but gets a prose poem instead because he's busy, or a poem if he's really busy, and *Three Moments of an Explosion*, perhaps, has that feel or vibe, in that some of the stories feel like fragments, sketches, notes of plots for longer works that will never get written. Lesser talents could write whole trilogies based on these ideas. No matter how short the piece, or the style – academic article, movie script, movie trailer, pastiche, parlour game rules, or just simply a complete story – the writing is as good and clear and crisp as we have come to expect from Miéville, and, as expected, I've added a few new words to my vocabulary.

We start at the beginning: a big bang from where the rest of the stories will flow, and 'Three Moments of an Explosion' is just that, three paragraphs describing an explosion and within that explosion "extreme squatters" – a mixture of bungee jumpers and Parkour enthusiasts are able to explore the building in extremely slowed down time as it explodes and collapses around them, but can they get out in time? From that explosion springs twenty-seven further fragments, some whole, some incomplete. In 'Polynia', the unbelievable has happened, icebergs have formed in the air above London and what else can you do but run through the streets with your mates watching as they form and hoping that a falling shard of ice the size of a house won't flatten you. But London is not alone, evidence from other environmental disasters have appeared in Brussels and Japan. The voice in this story is breathless and believable despite the fantastic nature of the central conceit.

'The Condition of New Death' is an article explaining the subjective, and yet objective condition of New Death, and what happens to corpses viewed by other people – no spoilers here, you'll just have to read the story or visit a morgue. In 'The Dowager of Bees' we are in the secret world of professional gamblers and a most unusual card game, in which unusual, and perhaps unwanted cards can appear. 'In the Slopes' at almost forty pages long is one of the longer works in the collection and recounts the exploits of two archaeological teams on a dig and how they preserve their finds of human and alien coexistence.

One of my favourite stories – and again this could easily have been a standalone novel – is 'The 9th Technique' which is one of the ten torture techniques outlined in a genuine US memo from 2002 outlining acceptable forms of interrogation. Seemingly, objects used in the interrogations (the cloth used in the first waterboarding is the Holy Grail of these items) have magical powers if called upon properly. Gruesome stuff, you might think, but the setting and the characters slide you into the tale before you know what's happening. It's a story that's a long way away from James Blaylock's *The Last Coin* and the coins once earned by Judas Iscariot. Other standout stories include the all-out horror of 'Sacken' and the outstanding, one-sided conversation 'The Buzzard's Egg'.

All in all, while great fun, entertaining, and thought-provoking, ultimately this is a slightly infuriating collection, but only infuriating because we just want more.

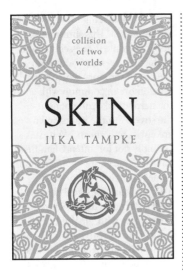

SKIN
Ilka Tampke
Hodder & Stoughton hb, 368pp, £12.99

Ian Sales

When is a Young Adult novel not a Young Adult novel? What is it that distinguishes YA fiction from that aimed at an adult readership? The age of the protagonist? Paul Atreides is fifteen years old when Frank Herbert's *Dune* opens, but the series has never been considered YA (or, as such books were known at the time, a "juvenile"). Perhaps it's that Young Adult fiction puts a romantic relationship front and centre, like the romantic triangle between Katniss, Gale and Peeta in Suzanne Collins' The Hunger Games trilogy. Or maybe it's the special snowflake status of YA protagonists – but then, to be fair, Paul Atreides also qualifies in that respect, very much so in fact.

Ilka Tampke's debut novel, *Skin*, sits somewhat uneasily on the borderline between YA and fiction aimed at an adult readership. Ailia, its protagonist and narrator, is a teenager for much of the book's length. She is initially attracted to an important young man in her village, but then falls in love with another, a mysterious

young man she stumbles across at the local river, who, bizarrely, has a large fish hook stuck in his mouth. And Ailia is certainly a special snowflake, so special her people even have a word for it, "Kendra", the mythical leader who will appear and save them all.

Ailia lives in Caer Cad, a small village in South-west Britain in 28AD. Her people are Celts, under imminent threat of invasion by the Romans. The novel's title is what these Celts call their totem animals. Except Ailia doesn't have one. She is a foundling, of unknown parents, so her "skin" remains unknown. This means she is barred from marriage – despite the importance of the aforementioned beau – and from education. She serves in the kitchen of her tribequeen and is, of course, the most competent and honest of the three girls who work there. Relations between the three later sour when a woman turns up asking for work, but Ailia turns her away after taking a dislike to her. The woman becomes a prostitute in the small slum outside the walls of Caer Cad, and later befriends one of the other kitchen girls, causing friction.

As is always the case with stories of this type, Ailia has a much greater destiny than her humble origins might suggest. Tampke paints an intriguing portrait of Iron Age Britain, although for reasons best known to herself she calls her druids "journeypeople". This, and other neologisms like "tribequeen" and "Cookmother", seem more whimsical than useful. Having said that, Tampke's version of the druidic religion in *Skin* is one of the novel's best elements. After Ailia has displayed some of her special snowflake abilities, she is reluctantly admitted to druid school. This involves a trip north to an island hidden on a mist-shrouded lake, where druid

candidates undergo wilderness training, and endure drug-fuelled trances so they can visit the Mothers' land, to learn the wishes of, and perhaps gain help from, the Mothers. The drugs don't work for Ailia but she has a much stronger connection to the Mothers than any druid. All this is fascinating and well-drawn, and by the far the best part of the novel.

Ailia follows a well-trod trajectory from foundling to saviour of her people. There is, of course, a price to be paid and – as is usual in books of this ilk, or perhaps even in YA novels – the price is romantic. It could be argued such bargains are banal, and that may explain their popularity in YA. But that would be doing *Skin* a disfavour. Tampke's novel could have been successfully marketed as YA, but Hodder chose not to do so – and the fact the book hovers somewhere on the border between the two marketing categories should not be held against it.

There are things to like between *Skin*'s covers. Perhaps, yes, Ailia is too special a snowflake to be sympathetic to an adult reader, and the skin concept is not really developed as much as expected given it provides the book's title. The relationships within the novel which also help define Ailia all seem a little too well-designed to provide emotional payoffs at the end, and while one such relationship is plausible, the number present in *Skin* does cause suspension of disbelief to totter somewhat.

However, Tampke's treatment of her milieu is interesting, and the Mothers, their land and Ailia's visits there, are especially good. While the romantic triangle, and especially the mysterious young man with the fish hook in his mouth, feels heavy-handed and threatens to overwhelm the jeopardy facing Ailia and Caer Cad, there's still more than enough in *Skin* for a reader to enjoy.

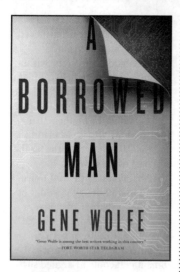

A BORROWED MAN
Gene Wolfe
Tor hb, 300pp, $25.99

Jack Deighton

The author carved out a well-regarded space for himself in the 1980s and '90s as a purveyor of quality high fantasy as in the various books of the New, the Long and the Short Suns, essayed a novel take on the unreliable narrator in his Latro in the Mist novels, made the occasional foray into detective/murder stories such as *Pandora by Holly Hollander*, and has also published various stand-alone books each with his own distinctive stamp, but in his previous output hasn't produced all that much in the way of straightforward SF. *A Borrowed Man* goes some way to altering that – but only some way – in that it has an impeccable Science Fictional premise in the shape of its narrator.

That narrator Ern A. Smithe, who is a reclone, having the consciousness of a long-dead author housed in a new version of his body, is a resource on a shelf in a library. Not legally human, fixed so as not to sire children, he can be consulted or even borrowed, but if he is not, then he will eventually be discarded and burned. He thinks real humanity has retired. For this is a world much diminished in population, with inhabitants who advocate further reductions; and reclones stand out. In this future society people with disabilities are kept out of sight to avoid troubling the rest, and what was the US is (to us) an unrecognisable set of fragmented states. However, as well as the reclones, there is advanced tech aplenty, voice-controlled cars and aircraft, robots of varying degrees of intelligence, but, despite the ubiquity of screens, books still exist – and inter-library loans, for clones as well as books.

Smithe is checked out of Spice Grove Public Library by Colette Coldbrook, whose father and brother are dead and who is the heiress to the estate. Smithe's original was the author of *Murder on Mars*, a book which formed the only contents of Conrad Coldbrook Snr's safe and which holds a secret. Both the Coldbrook men have been murdered and Colette thinks Smithe might know what that secret is. He doesn't, but he sets about finding out.

In what follows there is a degree of toing and froing across the country which, however, does not display many differences from the present; there are still, for example, bus stations and cross-country buses, on one of which Smithe takes up with a pair of misfits, Georges and Mahala, whose talents he makes use of.

The action keeps returning, though, to the Coldbrook house where the murders took place. It is run by robots and has a mini-nuclear reactor on one of the locked upper floors. There is also a door one steps through which takes Smithe to an alien world, light years away, peopled by strange, stick-like creatures and with menacing things coming out of the sea. This shimmer of SF gloss, while it does contribute to the plot, seems at odds with the rest of the story which has much more in common with the hardboiled thriller. For, if the streets Smithe walks down are not exactly mean, Wolfe has certainly not forgotten Chandler's Law; the one about having a man come through the door with a gun – even if this gun does have a strange trumpet shape. Encounters with the police and a confrontation with a man who is on his tail only heighten the film noir impression.

Frequently nowadays it can almost seem obligatory, but time was the SF detective story was a stunted beast, neither of the strands marrying well. In those terms *A Borrowed Man* just about falls on the right side of the line.

For an opening line, "Murder is not always such a terrible thing" is quite arresting. It is a true enough indicator of what follows, especially in signposting the thriller nature of the book as a whole, but doesn't quite deliver what it seems to promise while still presaging Smithe's sympathy for one of the murderers.

Notwithstanding the above, which can all be looked at as a species of excessive nitpicking, Wolfe writes like a dream. Smithe is an engaging and resourceful character and on the whole *A Borrowed Man* is immensely readable. It is all very cleverly done, and the plot is tied up without loose ends. As a detective story it works well and the SF elements are intriguing, but while the "borrowed human" concept is an ingenious one it is not really fully developed, despite Smithe meeting, in various libraries, different copies of his one-time wife, poet Arabella Lee. There is, though, apparently a sequel in the works.

THE MULTI-AWARD-WINNING AUTHOR
JAMES P. BLAYLOCK
STEAMPUNK LEGEND

BENEATH LONDON
A TALE OF LANGDON ST. IVES

BENEATH LONDON
James P. Blaylock
Titan pb, 416pp, £7.99

Jim Steel

Blaylock, famously, along with K.W. Jeter and Tim Powers, is one of the holy trinity that is credited with inventing steampunk (they didn't, of course, but Jeter named it) and, of the three, Blaylock is the one who has clove most closely to the genre. This is, by some reckoning, the tenth novel in a mostly-Victorian series that shares many characters.

Professor Langdon St. Ives will be particularly familiar to regular readers and is, once again, one of the heroes of this adventure. He vanishes off-screen for much of the time, sometimes literally as he chooses to investigate an enormous sinkhole that has appeared in the Victoria Embankment. There he discovers a vast cavern beneath London that is filled with enormous fungi possessed of strange powers. However, despite the title of the novel, we spend remarkably little time down there. Most of the action takes place on the surface where several other characters take up the running. Why such an inviting environment is not

explored further is a mystery. Jeff VanderMeer's loose Ambergris trilogy pretty much exhausted the possibilities of a (dare I say) mycelian culture, and it is possible that Blaylock wished to avoid the same territory. It's a pity because Blaylock's world even has its own Alice in the Professor's wife, the capable Alice St. Ives.

Blaylock has a clear style with anachronistically short, crisp sentences. The occasional archaic adverb such as "gainfully" might be dropped in by way of disguise, but this is a fast-paced thriller that owes as much to later pulp adventures as it does to the monsters of Victorian literature. The prose is masterful in its very transparency, and this leaves Blaylock free to drop in references to the likes of Tennyson without having to worry about losing the reader.

The early chapters with Beaumont the dwarf, down on his luck and mixing it in Dickensian squalor, sets a somewhat misleading tone. Perhaps because of it, Beaumont, at least at this stage, is one of the few characters with the free time to display much in the way of an inner life.

We soon venture out of London to Aylesford and the surrounding woods where much villainy is afoot. A witch-woman is decapitated, another, Clara, blind but psychic, is kidnapped, and murder is committed. Then it's back to London. While the Professor explores the sinkhole, others try to find the girl.

The real villain of the piece turns out to be a classic mad scientist called Klingheimer who has discovered that human heads can be sustained by the stumps of mushrooms. Naturally he has access to an asylum in order to procure experimental subjects. And equally naturally he is searching, with some success, for the elixir of life. One of his

other quests is for St. Ives' serial nemesis, Doctor Narbondo, who may have vanished beneath London. These multiple quests draw the other characters toward him in plotting that is as well-engineered as a pilfered pocket time piece.

Blaylock is clearly having fun with the characters. There is a Mister Bingham, for example, and an elephant called Ben Johnson. There is a wicked character called Maurice de Salles whose name must be a hat-tip to the famous Marquis. (But does that make Hillman, who is sometimes called Penny, a walking Benny Hill pun? Surely not. I may not be worthy of this novel.)

Some of the flaws are from decades ago and Blaylock couldn't fix them without going back and rewriting most of his back catalogue (and that way lies madness), but they are minor ones. The occasional name – whether of character or location – that doesn't sit well; the occasional person who seems to be lumbered with a floating accent. For many readers (especially the further they are from London) this will not present a problem. And we are all travelling away from the nineteenth century, so few of us can claim to be real experts.

At times it may feel as if Blaylock is coasting, but that can be put down to an over-familiarity with some of the characters. *Beneath London* is still miles ahead of most of the competition out there (and there is an awful lot of it now). It wears its research lightly, as it should, but one gets the impression that it would be a more than adequate guidebook for anyone wanting to find their way around certain areas of the London of 1884. Anyone wandering into Blaylock's novels for the first time could also do worse than start here.

LASER FODDER
TONY LEE

Full of green eggs and hammy acting, **CONTAMINATION** (Dual Format, 6 July) is a cheesy Italian splatter movie, basically like a drunken nightmare under the influences of *Alien*, *Invasion of the Body Snatchers* and *The Incredible Melting Man*. Made in 1980, it starts with a cargo ship that brings gory death to Manhattan island, and ends with an unlikely trio of heroes – a female colonel, a former astronaut (Ian McCulloch), and a New York detective – smashing the extraterrestrial conspiracy headquartered in Colombia. It rattles along from uncanny discoveries to exploding-people outrage and supposedly authoritarian reactions, but nothing in this psych/bio incursion from Mars really works as serious drama like *The Andromeda Strain*. It is only effective as exploitation cinema with occasionally surrealistic tableau, such as the inhabited polar ice-cave on Mars, or that glowing hypnotic eye of a drooling cyclopean monster in the South American finale.

Director 'Lewis Coates' (alias of Luigi Cozzi) has no finesse with SF, or realistic horror for that matter. So, like his earlier *Starcrash* (1978) and later *Hercules* (1983), this is frequently campy schlock blundering through a patchwork of clichéd revelation and modest surprises, until viewers surrender to its foreign lunacy or give up in tired dismay at its blatant rip-offs and shameless (politely anti-American?) references. One Anglophile riff is the Barranquilla-based company 'UniverX', which seems like a pun on Universal Exports from 007 movie *Live and Let Die*, and *Contamination* also redraws that Bond adventure's 'invisible' poppy fields scene, but with a fresh crop of alien eggs found hidden on a plantation.

Even with its Goblin soundtrack (average!) and a superb hi-def mastering job, this quite trashy effort is worth seeing only if you're an obsessive B-movie completist.

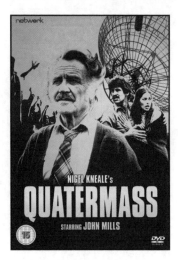

If you usually find that Leos Carax's work is excessively bizarre or wilfully unapproachable, prepare to be bored as this month's acutely art-house oddity from Swedish director Roy Andersson, alleged black comedy **A PIGEON SAT ON A BRANCH REFLECTING ON EXISTENCE** (DVD/Blu-ray, 13 July) is a challenge to viewers' tolerance for Fellini-haunted Bergman tributes. *Pigeon* is the last part of a trilogy, including *Songs From the Second Floor* (2000) and *You, The Living* (2007), that explore via highbrow whimsy and some mildly grotesque farce what it means to be human. But that's like trying to cast shadows on a broken mirror.

As you might expect, a static camera gives everything a stage-bound look, even street scenes, while tragicomic episodes about death, social awkwardness and several disastrously obscure political commentaries are foisted upon us by (amongst others) a Laurel-and-Hardy pair of terribly unfunny joke-salesmen in a rough mix of clumsy, crude and cryptic 'satire' that's never worth all the trouble of unpacking its meaning. Gentle surrealism becomes a Pythonesque skit as King Charles XII with royal troops in full costume regalia take a break from war marches and, with their unsubtly elitist manners, invade a quiet pub.

Elsewhere in Andersson's absurdist compendium of over three dozen sketches, there is Kafkaesque melancholy involving blithely vague shopkeepers, and a startling sequence of picturesque torture as slaves are herded into a metal cylinder that slowly revolves over a fire-pit. Unfortunately this one spectacle of claustrophobic industrial horror (composed, reportedly, as an historical critique of a mining company) cannot save the whole movie from its longueurs of unimpressive theatre, where "I'm happy to hear you're doing fine" is like a telephonic mantra of cultural decay on the grinding treadmill of temporarily modern life.

In spite of its cumbersome title, **THE ADVENTURES OF BUCKAROO BANZAI ACROSS THE 8th DIMENSION** (Blu-ray, 20 July) remains W.D. Richter's super-fun pop-cult masterpiece, partly inspired by *Doc Savage: The Man of Bronze* (1975) and *Invaders From Mars* (1953), with a weird sci-fi plotline emerging from Earl Mac Rauch's scratch-built comic-book style milieu about rock 'n' roll scientist heroes. "I've been ionised, but I'm okay now."

For the uninitiated, Peter Weller fronts as celebrity polymath Buckaroo, whose Team Banzai (including Jeff Goldblum, Clancy Brown, Lewis Smith and Pepe Serna) are experimenting with a fantastic jet-car to break the interdimensional barrier and end up fighting body-snatching villains in an alien race-war (of blacks versus reds), as Lectroids led by evil Dr Lizardo, alias Lord John Whorfin (John Lithgow at his manic best), reveal their genocidal plans against the Earth. This movie often moves very fast indeed, charging through a wildly imaginative scenario in a universe of half-surreality with rom-com diversions and half-madness where "Nothing is ever what it seems, but everything is exactly what it is". While this

champions the human spirit of adventure and revels in the necessity of vain fantasy in our culture, it also recognises that Planet 10's derision of mankind as 'monkey boys' has sagely authentic merit, if only as social criticism. "If you fail, we will be forced to help you destroy yourselves," warns an alien oracle, to chivvy things along a bit.

Alien spacecraft resemble giant bugs made of coral (a decade before *Babylon 5* designs), and Lectroid tech is a retro-fit mishmash of scavenged makeshift gear that's even messier than the unusual skiffy hardware depicted in Terry Gilliam's movies. As political satire, *Buckaroo Banzai* is broadly farcical: "Let's not panic" (good advice for galactic hitch-hikers) hears a US president under pressure to start a nuclear conflict, and the comment is promptly followed by a red alert with flashing lights

and security sirens. This launched Weller's genre career into such varied productions as *RoboCop*, *Leviathan*, *Naked Lunch*, *Screamers* and the vastly underrated TV series *Odyssey 5*, so his guest-star appearances in *24* and a couple of *Star Trek* incarnations met with fandom's approval. Alongside similar pictures of decidedly quirky humour, like *Repo Man* and *Big Trouble in Little China*, this helped to define the New Wacky cinema for the 1980s, and some unique visual jokes (dialogue is endlessly quotable) in *Buckaroo Banzai* ensure the movie is unbearably iconic today. While genre historians continue debating whether Banzai's oscillation over-thruster was invented before Doc Brown's flux capacitor, Buckaroo's influence extends into 21st century adventuring, as seen in *The Life Aquatic With Steve Zissou*.

Based on stories from the cult French comic book known in USA as *Heavy Metal*, TV anthology **METAL HURLANT CHRONICLES** (DVD/Blu-ray, 20 July) is a major, almost massive, disappointment. The six episodes of its first season comprise generic 1970s plots, some 1980s sci-fi cinematic styling, and twisty endings that fail to match the ironies of 1990s shows like *Babylon 5*. Whether presenting tragedy or comedy, or a mix of the two, there's more telling than showing here, and its level of predictability is equalled by a turgid semi-catatonic pace lacking any post-cyberpunk verve and just settling for pulpy space opera or faux barbarian adventures. Its makers never actually bother even trying to live up to the promise of some vividly colourful sketches in its title sequence. Gross

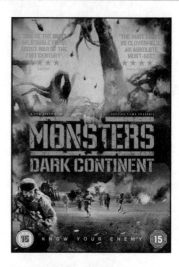

inadequacies at nearly every level seem likely to induce cringing fits in genre-literate viewers. It barely even qualifies as a guilty pleasure.

There's some variety to be found in the SF differences between a bunker drama for James Marsters (Spike in *Buffy* and *Angel*) and Michelle Ryan (*Bionic Woman* remake) in *Shelter Me*, and the inevitable outcome of a quest for an alien oracle by space hero Hondo (Joe Flanigan, *Stargate: Atlantis*) in *Master of Destiny*. But, as Hondo's adventure features a sexy assassin played by Kelly Brook, and another space episode – *Three on a Match* – harks back to *Cold Equations*, the variable scope/scales and fan appeal of this Euro production add up to damn little when its producers so readily fall back on typecasting (as blatant as Rutger Hauer's priest of exposition and Dominique Pinon's comic relief role) or commit familiar blunders, as when the asteroids wander about space closer together than wind-scattered traffic cones, and the punch line of a particularly uninteresting identity-mystery is just a defrosted Walt Disney. If this was dancing it would be amateur break or keep-fit belly, not classical ballet.

Made while the Apollo-Soyuz handshake in orbit still had political currency, the space disaster that marks the beginning of the end for **QUATERMASS** (Blu-ray/DVD, 27 July) is a typically bad omen of 'primal disorder' that shifts an ongoing international chaos to the very brink of apocalypse. Looking for his runaway granddaughter, Prof Q is older and wiser, yet often seen here as dishevelled and ranting with scathing commentaries (intellectual armour for his aged frailty) about overly politicised American and Soviet technocrats. However, John Mills' performance is gentlemanly as the calm rationality and scientific curiosity – a questioning nature that maintains his sanity – at the centre of national madness and global catastrophe for a generation of youths that represents an increasingly gloomy future.

Astronomer Dr Joe Kapp

(Simon MacCorkindale, star of telly superhero show *Manimal*) lives in a rundown observatory with two radio scope dishes – dubbed cat and dog – near Neolithic stones that fascinate his archaeologist wife and bewitch local teenagers. Unlike violent gangs engaging in gun terrorism on the streets, the "planet people" are gypsy hippies led by delusional but charismatic punk prophet Kickalong (a character reportedly inspired by Charles Manson). Instinctively following ley lines these doomed kids are lured to ancient sites of destruction. The planet people are mindlessly chanting blanks whose urgent insistence "Stop trying to know things!" is amusingly countered later by an old biddy's more plaintive "You've got to look after your brain".

Barbara Kellerman (as Kapp's wife), Margaret Tyzack (a sympa-

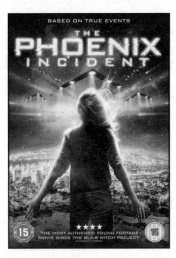

thetic authority figure) and Brenda (*Casualty*) Fricker are notables among the supporting cast, which includes David (*Chinese Detective*) Yip as Kapp's assistant Frank Chen. Also, look out for 1980s pop star Toyah Willcox (*Jubilee, Quadrophenia*) in a minor role.

Frequent sounds of gunfire in the distance seems like a narrative riff upon the Talking Heads song *Life During Wartime* (also first released in 1979), particularly as – double negatives aside – David Byrne's lyrics "this ain't no party / this ain't no disco / this ain't no foolin' around" fits this classic TV show's depiction of urban anarchy in London wastelands where books are useful only as paper logs for nightly fires ("What good are notebooks?" "The burning keeps me alive" chimes in Byrne).

Although the science heroes tend to disregard the self-destructive beliefs of the planet people's lemming-like behaviour, their mild atheism maintains/demonstrates an unhealthy respect for religious traditions. This, of course, sets up the grand finale, as science stings 'god', when the reinvigorated Quatermass eventually baits a nuclear trap for the vast unknowably-alien machinery's programmed attempts at genocide via "lovely lightning"

under vomit-green skies. Weird sci-fi concerned with a harvesting of humans is a genuinely Lovecraftian trope recently recycled in *Jupiter Ascending*. But what remains compelling about Nigel Kneale's bitterly composed vision of dystopia is that it stands in opposition to fellow Englishman Arthur C. Clarke's optimistic view of encounters with ET AI. These long buried machines in *Quatermass* (and let's include *Quatermass and the Pit*) are the antithesis of *2001*'s monolith. It is a chilling notion of ancient astronaut visitationism that Spielberg adopted for his *War of the Worlds* remake, and yet the cosmic horrors of Lovecraft are blended more perfectly here with Wellsian interplanetary conflict, and the result is gothic flavoured TV SF at its finest.

This welcome HD release of *Quatermass* presents the restored original serial (215 minutes, aspect ratio 4:3), suffused with an impeccably dramatic quality that is, inevitably, far less brisk than almost ruinously abbreviated movie *The Quatermass Conclusion* (106 minutes in widescreen) included as bonus material for this two-disc package, but the television edition is much more darkly atmospheric and charmingly characterful.

"We're gonna make a great team." When considering male and female partnerships in TV series like *The Mentalist, Castle, Bones, Lie to Me, Elementary* and *Monk* (for its comedy) a good if not strong case might be made that many such shows are sci-fi and fantasy to some degree. If not for their obvious genre content, as in *The Avengers* and *The X-Files*, then at least for the crooked genius of hideously complex schemes, or the uber-competence, and crime-solving prowess, of heroes that far exceeds the expertise of real-world cops. Created by Jon Bokenkamp, **THE BLACKLIST** (Season 2, Blu-ray/DVD, 17 August) is a slick mix of hi-tech gadgets and low-life cunning, a stylish crime drama with fast-moving action that plays like a super-charged version of *White Collar* (itself a brokerage updating of late 1960s TV show *It Takes a Thief*), but with mixed leads instead of two men and boosted towards an international spectacle by CIA black ops.

James Spader brings a lot more to his archly compelling super-crook character Raymond 'Red' Reddington than just a clotheshorse for expensive tailoring. His voice (well cast as Marvel's mad robot in *Avengers:*

Lively comedy starring Gillian Anderson and Ben Kingsley, **ROBOT OVERLORDS** (DVD/Blu-ray, 10 August) turns post-invasion clichés into a sci-fi sitcom with a jolly-good-fun ambiance throughout this modestly composed adventuring for British kids. Human collaborators enable alien dominance of citizens security-tagged under house arrest, until electroshock grants plucky teens freedom to play during urban curfew. If the walking tanks, flying drones and spidery snipers posing ED-209 style threats are not menacing enough, then cuboid Borgish motherships hovering in arrays all around the world stifle any rebellion from the defeated population. However, the occupation is not quite that fearsome. It's a photo-real cartoon of *Transformers* meets *Independence Day* action but with *Red Dawn* heroics of psychic boy versus Cylonistas claiming benevolent galactic 'police action' in our overwhelmed world's favour. They could have automated the Earth, if it wasn't for those pesky kids!

Like director Jon Wright's previous effort *Grabbers*, this is a low-budget imaginative treat wearing its genre derivative credentials as a proverbial badge of honour. There's nothing particularly original about its blatant coming-of-age material, and it lacks the hectic freshness of Joe Cornish's *Attack the Block*, but *Robot Overlords* is still highly enjoyable because Anderson and Kingsley are wonderful as their amusingly contrived oppositional characters.

Age of Ultron) often hints at a burden of haunted existence, and as Red his bogus vulnerability is shielded by magnificently weaponised sarcasm and bobbleheaded Spader's patented smarm-gasms of bemusing irony. His focused gaze seems to give people heatstroke or frostbite, whether enemies or friends. Red volunteers as a federal informant with sights on a complete immunity, but when he's adopted as the primary asset/resource of a new taskforce Red will only talk to FBI rookie profiler Liz Keen (Megan Boone). Like a Hannibal Lecter crossbred with Dr Mabuse, he's a smooth talking con man who feigns interest in trivialities just to mask his agenda or his vendor concerns as the infamous "concierge of crime".

Capable of monstrous acts and yet still willing to pursue redemption, bringing corporate terrorists and 'most wanted' or mug-shot celebs to book, Red refuses to be just a typically eccentric consultant (like Sherlock in *Elementary*), partly because that would severely limit his opportunities for creepy menace. Red will help to catch serial killers but later goes on a murder spree himself, only endangered by pithy quips to his betrayers. In the murky grey area of a global war zone between justice and vengeance, this show explores the delirium of trust – with codenamed villains like the Freelancer, Stewmaker, Alchemist, Scimitar, Decembrist, etc.

General Ludd is about a vigilante attacking capitalism conspiracy narratives. It pits DARPA against Hydra, as various nasty 'Hot War' developments of the proverbial military-industrial complex are stolen or corrupted by a comic-bookish rogues gallery of criminal networks presented as a jigsaw puzzle with too many pieces either missing or unknown to guess the complete picture. Episodes skate across differences between facts and truth, and identity, whether on paper or in genetics, becomes fluid reality. Pete Townshend's song 'White City' notes that blood is "analysed, as though it were fiction" and here family ties write – and edit (with admin privileges) – the realities of stories behind plots and plans. Does the habitually crooked Red intend to corrupt his own (surrogate?) daughter? There is more than a smidgen of *Alias'* family warfare in *The Blacklist*'s cross-genre makeup.

Of course, there are other mysteries behind supporting characters, especially Liz's apparently innocent husband, but thankfully soap opera secrets are kept in the margins, although some emotional impacts are often weakened by the awful cliché of blandly maudlin pop songs playing over otherwise quietly reflective scenes. The show boasts an impressive line-up of guest stars: Jane Alexander, Isabella Rossellini, Tom Noonan, Alan Alda, Jon Glover, Mary-Louise Parker (as Red's ex-wife!), Peter Fonda, Ron Perlman, Amanda Plummer, and Lance Henriksen. Harry Lennix (*Man of Steel*) is good value as Liz's federal boss Cooper.

Two-parter *Anslo Garrick* remixes *Die Hard* thrills with Bond movie intrigues. *The Cyprus Agency* explores heinous crimes centred on a fertility clinic (and it recalls *Coma*) where illegal adoptions spawn a probably toxic legacy. *Milton Bobbit* is about an obsessive character, seemingly imported from an *X-Files* tale, who freakily recruits assassins. In the debut season's two-parter finale Peter Stormare plays a top Russian baddie (with a hit-list of his own!) named Berlin who sticks around for early episodes of season two, where the assignment of a female Mossad agent to the FBI taskforce is an addition obviously copied from TV show *NCIS*.

"Value loyalty above all else" becomes the driving principle of Red's decision making, and yet his "Fulcrum" project is a blackmailer's info-dump that would expose a cabal of elite one-percenters led by the anonymous Director (David Strathairn). One episode about illegal organ transplants includes lethal product recall not unlike movie *Repo Men*. Another crazy doctor performs mind-control experiments, making people turn violent by exploiting a genetic anomaly. So before you can say MK-Ultra, Liz and Red are neck-deep in redacted files and in need of a polyglot. It leads to a hostage-at-gunpoint crisis with particular social relevance to actual shootings in the USA. When bio-terrorism meets suicide cult *The Front* threatens to unleash a GM plague. While investigating poachers our agents discover a hunter in Alaska whose hobbies include replaying *The Most Dangerous Game*.

A two-parter about brute *Luther Braxton* (spoilt by glaring lens-flare) features a secret prison on an oil-rig platform just like in *Face/Off*. Its psychodrama climax is composed of extended flashbacks to Liz's infancy, for blocked-memory retrieval, and a rather large piece of the back story's jigsaw puzzle (which astute viewers might have already guessed in the first season) finally drops into place.

The Major is one of the better clip-shows of recent years, as its compendium of flashbacks weigh the accumulated evidence (which of course sounds like a conspiracy theorist's heaven) that might expose the FBI taskforce and cover-up of Red's ongoing informal relationship with Liz, and the misuse of US governmental

detente resources to expand his empire. It has a satirical edge sharp enough to shave truth from fiction, in a storyline that even has a solid role for Liz's otherwise useless ex-husband Tom. *The Longevity Initiative* sees our extralegal heroes investigating secret research into immortality that uses jellyfish genes. In *Karakurt* there's a Russian assassin who can kill with just a touch.

Scenarios throw out offbeat terms like "five-sided foxhole" (the Pentagon) and "abduction mogul" with sufficient frequency to suspect original coinage in a few cases.

The Blacklist revisits Vernean extrapolation not Wellsian speculations, and the series upends spy-fi conventions as Red becomes like a Bond villain recast as unlikely hero. Red quotes Orwell and comments "What a visionary, but… his books are a downer". Red also quotes Bruce Lee and (more typically!) Shakespeare. At times, Red fancies himself a Byronic antihero, albeit with extra jabber. Some of his vague humanitarian concerns occasionally echo Spader's impassioned speeches as lefty liberal Alan Shore in comedy-drama *Boston Legal*, but Red's control freak machinations won't leave an important decision to any judge, or very many personal/professional choices for Liz.

Liz's tactical options become increasingly desperate in a head-spinning pursuit of whatever negotiable truth is out there, but she's often lost in a world where "there are no sides. Only players". Our baffled heroine endures several *24*-style days, and yet she appears in danger of enjoying her condition as a lifelong victim of Big Plot. As the season closes, a haunted, overstressed Liz finally remembers her childhood's tragedy. Season three starts in October. Titan publishes the spin-off comic of original stories.

A delightfully named world cinema label, Mr Bongo releases two classics from Polish surrealist Wojciech Has on Blu-ray, in rarely seen black-but-nifty cases, 7 September. Ostensibly, Has' **THE SARAGOSSA MANUSCRIPT** (1965) is a 175-minute movie set in the Napoleonic wars, but there's far more to this epic than meets the eye or ear. Muslim sisters seduce adventurer Alfonse, but he wakes up in a graveyard to find that they were only a dream (or perhaps he was just the lesbians' fantasy?) or very friendly ghosts. Was our fearless captain of guardsmen beguiled by succubi? Alfonse plots his safe route home to Madrid. "That's my plan and nothing is going to change it!" Caught by surprise (well, nobody expects the Spanish Inquisition!), noble hero Alfonse is arrested for his sins. As one of the many stories nested within other stories, there's a honeymoon in a haunted castle, and the tales unpack with slight confusions, usually of tone, as panto slapstick competes with gallows humour in an episodic maze of narrative culminating in a grand loop – a critique of religious piety, sitcom routines of coincidence, a romantic farce capering through many historical diversions between moral dilemma and elaborate charade? Whatever its meaning, this is certainly a witty twist on Munchausen's tales, with a fractal narrative that dovetails or explodes with a whimsical ambiguity, and a unique, although somewhat Bunuelian, widescreen style.

One of the neglected masterpieces of surrealist cinema, **THE HOURGLASS SANATORIUM** (1973) is based on a collection of short stories by Bruno Schulz. The movie enjoys a gothic beginning as Jozef rides a ghost train to visit his ailing father in a rundown hospital. A flustered nurse explains that everyone sleeps in because "night never comes". This movie

is concerned with relativity, the complexity of dreams, and reliving memories. Like Vonnegut's Billy Pilgrim in *Slaughterhouse-Five* (filmed by George Roy Hill in 1972), protagonist Jozef is unstuck in time so, while looking out of a sanatorium window, he sees himself arrive. He can check out any time that he likes, but he can never leave. Jozef's dad is dead but "doesn't know or suspect" and so becomes chatty in his magical nest. Jozef's mother is confused (demented?) about life, as if taunted by fate. Weaving through nightmares of a Jewish ghetto and threats of warfare, Jozef wears a number of different hats (like Mr Benn!) to help define his role-playing in a variety of bewildering sequences. The cryptic dialogue

rings with poetic resonance as frequently stunning tableaux of decay emerge from left and right angles. A frustrated blind man opens his eyes to a Kafkaesque understanding of the world. Josef wanders a cobweb maze of maturity traps, or youthful fears, with portals for trippy escapes underneath displaced beds. A stamp album is as good a guidebook to this milieu as any map. In the theatre of waxy people on clockwork display, history unfolds in characters, while the baggage of hallucinations and grotesquery piles up to completely discredit narrative – whether linear or Escherian. Jozef hangs a kettle on a tap but cannot make the water flow.

This restored edition is quite exquisite. Any fans of Terry Gil-

liam and the Quay brothers (who filmed one of Schulz's stories in 1986 as animated short *Street of Crocodiles*) will doubtlessly love it.

Mr Bongo is also releasing an HD restoration of Fellini's **CASA-NOVA** (Blu-ray, 7 September). Made in 1976, this lavishly composed biopic stars Donald Sutherland, sometimes lost in all the colourful stage-craft magic, ornate symbolism and frivolous bed-hopping comedy of theatrical presentation and artistic pretension. Despite trying hard to amuse, this is merely a conventional historical drama (although the robot girl encounter obviously stands out as a genre sequence) of campy ballooning desire and farcical hi-jinks when compared to Has' pair of more exuberantly weird works.

GAZE CONTROL: ROUND-UP

A shockingly awful effort, **MONSTERS: DARK CONTINENT** (Blu-ray/DVD, 31 August) is a failed sequel in every way. A flatly dull scenario, with a batch of witless characters seemingly played by potted plants from a third-rate acting academy, sees middle-eastern military action stumbling through jittery camerawork and mumbled dialogue (and narration!), interrupted just two or three times by mindlessly noisy sequences of extraterrestrial beasties of various sizes. Clearly, these filmmakers wanted this to be seen as different to Gareth Edwards' original *Monsters*, but *MDC* has no effective style and even less genre substance. US troops sent into the desert are hunters that become hunted in the infected zone. One encounter is like something from a creature fea-

ture titled Esoteric Park but all the strangeness and credibility of *Monsters* is absent here. *District 9* and *Battle: Los Angeles* are superior.

KNIGHTS OF SIDONIA: COMPLETE SERIES ONE (DVD/Blu-ray, 17 August) is twelve episodes of sci-fi anime with a space opera plotline about aliens, the destruction of Earth, and mutant-human survivors living on an asteroid-spaceship.

The first movie from a maker of numerous videogames, Keith Arem's UFOlogy tract **THE PHOENIX INCIDENT** (DVD, 7 September) is a dreary bogus documentary where an unwatchability, roundly characterised by ticked boxes on a clichés checklist, sets in right from the start.

Although the *Highlander* franchise

dressed its immortality scenarios in freewheeling action of historical episodes time-slipped towards a kind of magic destiny, **THE AGE OF ADALINE** (Blu-ray/DVD, 14 September) is stuck in a sappy love story, with not even any trad or mod romantic adventure to enliven its lamentable chick-flick appeal. Blake Lively lets her clothes and hairstyles portray the ageless Adaline. Harrison Ford takes care of the proper acting in a thankless role as an old flame who can't forget her. Lee Toland Krieger directs with glum pretence at avoiding the accursed pigeonhole of generic sci-fi, although a cover blurb considers it's important to inform potential disc buyers that this comes "from the people that brought you *The Time-Traveller's Wife*". Well, the postman delivered my copies; if he gets the credit, who deserves the blame?

MUTANT POPCORN
NICK LOWE

Back before all this, it was enough to become a hero. Films were all about sacrificing what you thought you wanted in order to win what really mattered, bish bosh, return with the elixir, sorted. But now, you're a superhero or you're nothing. Soon not just the comics films, but every other film as well, will be about the acquisition of god-like powers and their correct use in saving the innocent at the price of your personal scores. If we're not quite at the point where the Marvel machine has eaten the sun, we're certainly hitting the point of no return. Of the twelve films here, at least half are superhero stories of one kind or another, most of them light variations on *Fantastic Four* #1. But at least there's one that stands out from the pack like an ox among chickens, and whose muscular engagement with these tropes owes nothing whatever to Hollywood narrative models or the comic-book cinema omniverse: a relentlessly incomprehensible three-hour black-and-white masterpiece half a century in the making, adapted from a Soviet sf classic by Tarkovsky's greatest contemporary and peer, and which killed its director and outlived more than one of its performers during seven years of post-production on top of a six-year shoot.

Before we go further, it needs to be said that Aleksei German's **HARD TO BE A GOD** requires some instructions for viewing. If your memory of the Strugatskys' 1964 novel is rusty, the narrative here will simply laugh at your trousers and steal your phone. Press viewers of the limited theatrical release were thoughtfully issued with a synopsis to assist them in the pretence of knowing what the hell they had just witnessed. But this is a film of a kind of greatness they don't make any more, and whose passing from the world may be felt by some with as

much relief as sorrow. Most people will watch this film interruptibly on a small screen, which is fine, but there's nothing like being trapped with these images in a dark space for three hours in real time with no opportunity to keep a finger in the novel to remind yourself who these characters are, which castle we're in, or what at any moment is going on.

For what help it may be, however, this is the story. On a feudal world teetering on the cusp between a looming renaissance and a tumble back into a centuries-long dark age, master swordsman and miracle-worker Rumata struggles to rescue the planet's beleaguered scholars and artists from local warlord Don Reba's brutal pogrom, part of a larger power struggle between the equally savage and fascistic Greys and Blacks (who look much

the same in monochrome). But what Reba doesn't know about his nemesis is that Rumata is actually Anton, a scientific observer from Earth who has stolen the identity of a deceased local aristocrat, and who finds his principles of non-intervention in conflict with his conscience as the world around him slides into darkness and his quest to rescue a local scientist from Reba's clutches precipitates a moral and personal crisis.

German died in 2013 and the surviving Strugatsky (Boris) the year before; the sound mix for German's final edit was completed by his widow and son, its weirdly random dialogue ("It's autumn; there are no mice. A goose drowned here") and voiceover often seeming deliberately off-sync or unrelated to the scene. But this seems to be part of the intended design, which actively relishes the

breaking of rules that have stood in cinematic mimesis for a century. The camera is constantly and casually acknowledged, and never sits still during the elaborately choreographed long takes, yet key action is often out of frame. Extras crowd the shot, gurn into the lens, and thieve the scene with dung-devouring village-idiot grins; and the whole thing looks like Bresson's *Lancelot du Lac* set-dressed by the young Terry Gilliam, with more mud, rain, entrails, and indeterminate filth than anyone has ever seen outside a farm holiday in County Mayo, and actual *Holy Grail* moments come to life in Brueghelvision on Planet Baldrick. ("They threw a cow on me," a character grumbles wanly. "From the bridge.") The novel's Earth-set prologue and epilogue have gone, and all technology is hidden; if it weren't for the sparse

If your memory of the Strugatskys' 1964 novel is rusty, the narrative here will simply laugh at your trousers and steal your phone

introductory exposition, you wouldn't know this wasn't an indeterminately thirteenth-century terrestrial game of middens.

It sounds unwatchable, but it's utterly compelling and immersive, with every shot a masterclass in old-school in-camera spectacle. In the end this is the one thing that diminishes the film relative to the book, because what the screen version doesn't have is the novel's intellectual and moral power – the uniquely science-fictional sense of standing hands-tied in the middle of an entire world's history with a godlike awareness of the stakes and a tormented mix of revulsion and

On the upside, the film has successfully delivered a visually credible shrinking-man film for today's 3D-conversion audiences

pity for the sufferings out of which civilisation is born. German trusts the viewer to bring all that if he merely provides the moral chaos and stomach-churning images, which is probably too ambitious an ask. But it's been so long since ambition in sf cinema was this big that we'd barely noticed how the pictures got so small.

Hard to Be a God had already wrapped but the Marvel Cinematic Universe was still a gleam in Kevin Feige's eye back when Edgar Wright started developing **ANT-MAN** for Marvel; and the expansion of the Universe during the seven years it took to get the production in front of a camera seems to have been the ultimate source of the tension that drove Wright off the project and the script into a frenzied rewrite to incorporate material like the clumsily inserted raid on Avengers HQ and the well-meant but

bathetic plunge into *2001* territory at the climax, both of which are the narrative equivalent of Kate Mara's wig in the *Fantastic Four* reshoots. Hank Pym's delayed entry to the MCU has forced a reshake of all kinds of canon elements from the main Avengerverse, pleasingly represented here in the 1989 prologue by guest stars in various states of digital and practical makeup. But to absolutely nobody's surprise, the overall result is a unwieldy cobble-up of the best of Wright's original set pieces (the briefcase fight and bedroom showdown), the worst of the MCU exobaggage he walked off his own film rather than accede to, and assorted bright ideas from the star and his co-writer – of which the most adventurously conceived and bathetically executed is the quantum detour in the middle of the climax to "a reality where all concepts of time and space become irrelevant", which some may feel we've already reached.

Early script leaks included an enormous first-act sequence in which ethical catburglar (let's not even try) Scott addresses his child-support woes through a series of shrink-suited stunts involving

ATMs, casinos, and lottery balls, all of which has been banished to the quantum realm in the release version, along with the film's most interesting character. But the middle act is still mostly protracted training montage, Evangeline Lilly's Hope is thrown only scraps and an IOU for a hopeful sequel, and we've probably by now had a couple more instances than we need of that Judy Greer mom character who is neither as fun nor as hot as the new hire. On the upside, the film has successfully delivered a visually credible shrinking-man film for today's 3D-conversion audiences, a useful comedic thread for future iterations of the Avengerverse, and a version of Ant-Man that can segue seamlessly into the *Civil War* footage in the credits, which is what all the huffing and fighting was about in the first place. But that's the lesson Scott learns in becoming a superhero: it's the little things that make the big differences.

Ant-Man's chuted-in director Peyton Reed had been in line for the keys to the Marvel washroom for some time, having lost out narrowly to James Gunn

for the *Guardians of the Galaxy* gig after previously working with MCU mastermind Feige on an version of **FANTASTIC FOUR** which Fox rejected. How everyone feels about that now can be imagined, as the *Fantastic Four* they went with instead finds itself the unbidden poster kid for all that's dysfunctional about studio filmmaking: the tyranny of release dates, intellectual-property renewal licences, and studio hive-thinking over considerations of basic coherence and reasons for audiences to want to see it. The battle for mastery of the blame narrative is still under way as we go to press, with Fox leaking hard about Josh Trank's inadequacies at the helm, while doing their best to bat away inconvenient counter-whispers about the studio's bullying and indecision on matters of story, budget, and casting. It's probably too soon to say nobody emerges with credit, because two figures at the centre of the storm who have stuck to their dignified silence are writer-producer Simon Kinberg and unconfirmed cleanup director Matthew Vaughn. But when the B-roll footage shows that there was a Fantasti-Car in the third act,

something's clearly gone a bit more adrift than a few character beats.

What's left, after what appears to have been a drastic reduction of the set-piece count, is an unexpectedly low-key blockbuster which by default leaves its watchable ensemble cast to shoulder most of the load that in more conventional, or better-made, superhero pictures gets hived off to action sequences and digital spectacle. The sub-*Green Lantern* digital alienscape is almost defiantly unattractive, and in the single most startling interdimensional story jump a whole year disappears from the middle of the film, taking with it not only a huge chunk of plot and the immediate emotional aftermath of becoming four godlike freaks, but all the obligatory demos of learning to use their powers. It's not a particularly good choice, but it does make for a different kind and shape of superhero origin story; and behind all the vagueness about the new Doctor Doom's actual powers are such striking sf ideas as a sentient planet and a third-act battleground where nobody quite knows how the laws of physics are locally warped. This cast clearly has a good FF film in them, and if

The Fantastic Four they went with instead finds itself the unbidden poster kid for all that's dysfunctional about studio filmmaking

Fox want to hang on to the rights for another round they could do a lot worse than fixing this iteration before thinking about a clean reinstall. This remains one of the great foundation myths in the world comics canon, the model for all subsequent group-empowerment origin tales, and the Ultimate version was a solid choice for the reboot. But to save it all from being raptured up into another universe, they're going to need to learn to work as a team.

TERMINATOR: GENISYS crashes through the roof of the franchise-reboot bandwagon by sending the second film back in time before the first one to terminate the original in the first act, with the good T-800 rescuing and raising Sarah Connor from 1973 so she can take out the bad one in 1984 and head forward with Kyle Reese to thwart Skynet's next attempt to come alive out of

the internet of things in 2017. It begins wonderfully, re-enacting sequences from the original with appropriate twists, and setting up a classic time-twister puzzle ending, where we're clearly going to go back to the original 1973 shootout (glimpsed only in fragments, with no shots of Sarah's mysterious father) and learn what the Terminators were doing there in the first place, probably with some poignantly ingenious self-sacrifice by Kyle to save Sarah for the future and issue the key line of advice that will save the future. The father is a particular challenge, because there doesn't seem anyone non-awkward for him to turn out to be. But the film has a more radical answer than any we were expecting: ditch that ending entirely, answer none of the questions posed, and sign the cast up for multiple films in the hope that the answers can be spun out to trilogy. The consequence has been exactly

the opposite of that intended: audiences have been so maddened by the non-resolution that we may never now see the answers promised, whereas if they'd just been tied up in this film we'd have had a new time-twister classic and a sequel would have been in the bag. It's a shame, because Emilia Clarke is a surprisingly good Sarah, if not much like Linda Hamilton, while Jai Courtney's version of Kyle is in contrast a complete bust whose death would have been just what the franchise needed to keep it alive. Still, first-weekend figures from China suggest the global fanbase may just have terminated the termination order and the post-credits tease may yet get cashed in after all. We may just need to go with it if we want to live.

It's back to the 8-bit eighties with a different avatar in **PIXELS**, Chris Columbus' feature expansion of Patrick Jean's famed two-minute short about an attack on Manhattan by vintage videogames. The original short had no characters or plot, and not everyone will welcome the acquisition of the property by Adam Sandler's people and its repurposing as a family

rom-com for a Sandler lead with *Ghostbusters* as its era-appropriate template. The internet is perfectly entitled to its loathing of Sandler and all his works, though one of the revelations of the festive Sony hack was the consistent value he's managed to deliver to the studio to which he remained, till the Netflix deal, unswervingly loyal, and at the very least he's an intelligent and committed team player who manages his somewhat restrictive brand thoughtfully and uses the broader commercial fare to subsidise projects closer to his personal taste. Sony, at least, have thrown in everything they have, including the struggling studio's other remaining in-house comedy asset Kevin James, whose *Paul Blart 2* has proved their top hit of a miserable year so far, and with quality support from Josh Gad and Peter Dinklage (who in a stroke of high-concept casting plays a version of gaming legend Billy Mitchell being played by Peter Dinklage, with a brilliantly cast teen version who looks unnervingly like a chibi Terminator). It's not a terrible combination, and there's a solid game engine in the gag premise about eighties arcade-warrior nerds

growing up to be the US President (James) and his less achieving mates. But it's one of those films where most of the trailer comes from the third act, and before we get to where the short got us in two minutes, we have to graduate through a protracted flirt-cute between Sandler and an out-of-his-league Michelle Monaghan, with forced life-wisdom from *Donkey Kong*: "I had my shot. Every time I try, that giant ape throws another barrel at me." By the end, you know how he feels.

Pixels features a strange robot cameo role for actor, director, and Pixar writer Tom McCarthy, who helped Pete Docter on *Up* and *Inside Out*, and has gone from well-regarded indie fare like *The Station Agent* and *Win Win* to direct Sandler's other underloved fantasy vehicle of the season in **THE COBBLER**. As a Sandler film, it's an unavoidably awkward attempt to fold elements of his comedic brand and persona into what is at its heart a sweetly cornball indie fable about Jewish identity and tradition. Sandler is on superior form in his baseline performance as a schlubby self-

employed nth-generation shoe guy conflicted between his heritage, his Alzheimery mom, his anger at his no-good vanished dad, and his own vague dreams to be anything but what he is, which suddenly come true when he inherits the power to assume the form of any customer by mending their shoes on his dad's magic stitcher. Now he can be Dan Stevens, Dustin Hoffman, McCarthy's *Wire* co-star Method Man, or rather all of the above playing Adam Sandler trying to play themselves; but in the film's edgiest and most effective sequences, it doesn't turn out as easy as that. Borrowed lives incurs costs and debts, risks and secrets you may not want to shoulder, and Adam soon finds out that other people's lives aren't necessarily anywhere you'd actually want to live. So early experiments with stalking women and mugging yuppies (for which he simply turns himself into a black guy) gradually give way to a realisation that he's living in a superhero origin story, that evil needs to be answered with good, and that using his superpowers to help the little guy, in a storyline close to Netflix's *Daredevil*, is more likely to score him a girlfriend

It's a film by actors about acting as a serious calling for budding superhoeroes, which tries to reach out to Sandler's core fans

closer to his league. Like it sounds, it's a film by actors about acting as a serious calling for budding superhoeroes, which tries to reach out to Sandler's core fans while still finding space for a prologue in subtitled Yiddish. It's an interesting ethnic side-shift for McCarthy, save for one cataclysmic misjudgment: the Method Man character, who comes over as a grotesquely stereotyped urban thug, is clearly set up to be revealed as a caring citizen crudely misread, but no, he's just a grotesquely stereotyped urban thug. The offensiveness of that lingers long after the rest of the film is forgotten.

The hazards of stepping into others' shoes is also the theme of Tarsem Singh's **SELF/LESS**, which serves up reheated seconds of *Seconds* in a younger, buffer physique. Sir Ben Kingsley is a hard-dealing but regret-fuelled celebrity architect who

Sir Ben Kingsley is a hard-dealing but regret-fuelled celebrity architect who buys himself a new life in Ryan Reynolds' body

buys himself a new life in Ryan Reynolds' body, only to find that being reborn as a puppy-eyed Canadian isn't quite the strings-free experience he was sold, and that it's no good being a driven, controlling, sociopathic billionaire tyrant if you don't ask the thumpingly obvious sf questions at point of sale. Fortunately his new body comes with action skills pre-installed, for reasons which will not long detain viewers of above-zero percipience, and we're all set for a game of cat and mouse in which they're after him and he's after them and there will be hiding out with attractive strangers and a showdown and sacrifice as he heroes up for the climax. Sir Ben learns about the secretive world of body-hopping by googling something called Shedding, which sounds like something suburban swingers do in their allotments but turns out harmlessly to throw up images of the late (*or is he?*)

Roger Lloyd Pack. But as the salesman confirms, life-extension is for all who are prepared not to read the licence agreement to the end: "Just think of all the great minds this world has lost because their bodies were failing. Einstein! Edison! Steve Jobs! Just think what he could have accomplished with another fifty years on this planet…" (Ben bites his new Canadian tongue: *Cars 3* through *12*, a self-riding bicycle, and a firmware store for sentient toasters.)

The major disappointment of *Self/Less* is that it's only about a 1.8 on the Tarsem scale, where *The Cell* and *The Fall* are a 5, *Mirror Mirror* an 8, and *Immortals* goes up to logarithmic 11. Aside from Sir Ben's astounding gold-fixtured interior design in an early set and a few bits of local colour in the New Orleans sequences, the film carefully eschews the decorative excess that's hitherto been most of the reason for watching his films, and the decease of legendary costume designer Eiko Ishioka seems to have prompted a move away from his signature visual style, leaving audiences with nothing to watch but the cast and story – which stops short of the obvious

further body-hopping payoff that you're expecting as the reward for watching. Surprisingly, given the pro-Obamacare plot thread that literate viewers will spot from early on, the end credits include a prominent "special thank you" to noted political comedian Donald Trump, his organisation and his tower. Just think what *he* could accomplish with another fifty years on this planet.

The metaphysics and ethics of human identity are pondered in Seth McFarlane deadpan in **TED 2**, a stoner courtroom dramedy about civil rights for sweary fuzzball thunderbuddies with superhuman bong appetites and a checklist of the qualities needed for magical friends to become icons of diversity and freedom: "self-awareness, an ability to understand complex emotions, and empathy", which coincidentally are precisely the things our overactive infantile theory of mind attributes erroneously to toys and other forms of manufactured and copyrightable property. This time around, Ted needs to be legally classified as a person rather than a possession so that he can adopt a child and also

outwit Giovanni Ribisi's continuing dastardly machinations in a madcap Comic-Con climax comprising a slapstick chase through the whole of popular culture.

Like the first film, of which it's a surprisingly coherent thematic amplification, it works hard at pumping the laughs out, and succeeds often enough to make up for the ones that flop down dead; but its real strength is in playing straight, making high-concept comedy from trying to trap you into projecting absurdly serious issues on to childishly stupid premises. How deeply McFarlane and his writers have thought about the edges of comedy and how to sail around them is shown by the bravura sequence where Ted and John amuse themselves at a comedy improv show by shouting out comedy-proof suggestions: "Bill Cosby!" "Ferguson!" "Charlie Hebdo!" "Robin Williams!" The ejection of Mila Kunis is initially a worry, but Amanda Seyfried turns out to be not only funnier but a serious musical asset, with a sincerely (or, wait, is it?) lovely song that would surely score McFarlane a cheeky Oscar nomination if it didn't come straight after a

weed joke about *Jurassic Park* and *Contact*. The film then drops in a gag that invites you to laugh at yourself for finding such manufactured sentiment affecting; but as Seyfried says in her passionately straight courtroom speech about civil rights and the legal definition of a person, delivered over a wish-animated magic bear, "Anyone who can inspire that kind of love in another person deserves to be called human." Got us again.

Another thought-experiment romcom unfolds in Terry Jones' **ABSOLUTELY ANYTHING**, which sees an alien council of quondam Pythons seeking to test humanity's capacity for good and evil by gifting tweedy teacher Simon Pegg with godlike powers and watching the hilarity unfold, with the fate of the Earth at stake if he fails to entertain. It sounds awful, and the opening titles get off to an unpromising start by misspelling "Intergalactic", but it's not a complete washout: Pegg gives the uneven material everything he's got, and grains of chemically pure comedy gold can be detected with the naked eye in the sequences where he plays off Robin Williams'

There are characters, motives, scenes, and lines that would make any observer despair of humanity's chance at salvation

semi-improvised talking dog. Nevertheless, there are characters, motives, scenes, and lines that would make any observer despair of humanity's chance at salvation. Kate Beckinsale is particularly tested here, as the overqualified love interest who openly defends Pegg – characterised by his boss as "irresponsible, idle, and feckless" – with such credence-benders as "He's not gay; he's likeable" and "He's attractive and he's kind." (Kate Beckinsale finds Simon Pegg attractive. Okayy.) Much of the script seems not to have been read out loud till it was filmed. When our hero blithely wishes that "Alien spaceships destroy 10C", the mass bafflement is audible; there's some token southern-US representation in the form of Beckinsale's unplayably-written stalker, but he's played by Rob Riggle who is quite audibly from Kentucky. When Pegg is called out on pretending to be blind, "I prefer the term optically challenged." No wonder he complains to the canine Williams: "Dennis, why do you let me say things like this?" That's right, blame it on the dog.

Empowerment by a quintet of brightly-coloured string-pullers is also the theme of **INSIDE OUT**, in which Pete Docter continues his attempt to reverse-engineer the Miyazaki magic by here returning to the inspiration for *Spirited Away*: an animator's daughter passing from the goofball joy of primary innocence into the more subdued and grumpy tweens. 11-year-old Riley, like Docter himself, is uprooted from Minnesota to San Francisco, and her Pixar-style brains trust comprising five of the six Ekman emotions (Surprise having been quietly consigned to the pit of oblivion) have to steer her through the upheaval while team leader Joy is stranded on the edge of Riley's crumbling inner world with only her dumpy and unloved sister Sadness to help. It's a hugely ambitious and resonant concept, and one can't but wish it well, but the execution is thinner than might have been hoped, with the visual landscape of the mind rather sparsely designed, and a plot environment that feels a little too much like an early learning game set in a theme park of the self. Though a lot of real research on emotion and personality has gone in, not a lot of it comes out again; the film's use of cognitive and emotion science is cherry-picked and at times pretty questionable, and its baleful implication that childhood emotional intelligence is lost forever when the puberty button gets hit is both false and faintly malign – as is the conclusion that sadness has a legitimate role but only as a precursor to joy. But it's a wonderful thing that all over the planet children are playing with action figures of Sadness and Fear, and that

every preschooler's style pinup is breakout favourite Disgust.

Inside Out came about after Docter was parachuted in to replace veteran sound wizard Gary Rydstrom on his feature debut *Newt*, only to swap in his own project and send Rydstrom's to the back of the fridge, after a long association with Pixar extended all the way back to their early years at Lucasfilm before Steve Jobs bought the division out in 1986. (Rydstrom was the sound man on *Luxo Jr.*, and had graduated to directing a couple of their shorts as well as inheriting Docter's gig as director of the Studio Ghibli dubs from *Earthsea* onwards.) But Pixar's loss has been his old employer's opportunity, and Lucasfilm have snapped Rydstrom up instead for the delicate job of nursing George Lucas's **STRANGE MAGIC** to screen. Fairy princess Evan Rachel Wood finds herself Ashley Madisoned by her Prince Hans of a fiancé on their wedding day, and immediately renounces love in favour of mauve eyeliner and kinda-hot fairy outdoor wear, only to tumble into a jukebox fairy musical plot stitched together from a garbled memory of *A Midsummer Night's Dream* and a slightly less Stockholmy version of *Beauty and the Beast*.

Initially it seems like it's going to be just horrific, with a sexual dimorphism that requires the fairy females to be hideous Barbie-headed mutants with insectoid waists and giant horror eyes, and Alan Cumming's Bog King (I know…) lording over a dark kingdom of toad-textured slime and insect people, while the only black character is a troll-haired midget in urban dungarees who sings Marley and is driven by his inappropriate pining for an uptown blonde princess to head over to the dark side of the wood to score some party drugs from the, ahem, "sugar

plum fairy". But once your eyes adjust to the gruesome design, it starts to deconstruct the pat polarities of fairy narrative in favour of a positive celebration of diversity and cross-tracks romance. ("I've learned a valuable lesson: never judge someone or something by how he or she or it looks.") Unfortunately the world's judgment on the film has been less forgiving.

For serious strangeness and magic, though, the fairy animation to beat is Tomm Moore's **SONG OF THE SEA**, which offers largely the same plot as *Inside Out* with Irish fairy lore in place of head science, and the gorgeous Celtic 2D stylising from *The Secret of Kells* now spread across a wider range of canvases, including contemporary cityscapes and windswept Atlantic crags alongside the enchanted woods and meadows. Lighthouse-keeper's son Ben and his silent selkie sister, forcibly exiled to the city from their Ponyoesque cliff by the sea, run away from their ghastly granny to find their path home, uncover the mystery of their mother's disappearance, and in the process free the Shee and save the otherworld from a villain who deals with pain by decanting emotions into sealed jars. Their extraordinary road trip through faerie is propelled by a potent Yeatsian pull of longing and mystery, leading to a character with a beard made of plot strands and a climax where the whole of Celtic myth comes to life. There are beautifully animated tears that fall upward, a Miyazaki flying scene, a Kellsified Tate & Lyle lion, illuminated jellyfish, rocks with faces and eyes that open, and even the obligatory dodgy musical numbers are redeemed at the end by an amazing rewind to storyboard under the final credits. If this is how the old gods and first heroes see our world, no wonder they find it hard to leave.